THE LEGEND OF ARDNAMURCHAN

THE ARDNAMURCHAN CHRONICLES

KAY GILL

TRESOR
PRESS

To Andrew. Thank you for everything.
And some wonderful people: Ross, Esther, José, Sonny,
Frances, Amy, Ben, Leo, Felicity, Sam, Natalie, Seth, Caleb,
and Eden-Rose.
And some wonderful dogs (sea hounds): Tyson (RIP) and
Bonnie.

CONTENTS

GLOSSARY

Bairn (Scots) – baby or child

Bampots (Scots) – idiots

Ben (Gaelic) – mountain

Blethering (Scots) – gossiping

Bogging / boggin (Scots) – disgusting and smelly

Bubbly-jock (Scots) – male turkey

Cannae (Scots) – cannot

Clamhan (Gaelic) – buzzard

Didnae (Scots) – didn't

Dinnae (Scots) – don't

Doolally (Scots) – crazy

Dram (Scots) – a tot, or a small measure of whisky

Drookit (Scots) – soaking wet

Dunderheids (Scots) – idiots

Faileas (Gaelic) – reflection

Laddie (Scots) – boy

Laird (Scots) – landowner

Lassie (Scots) – girl

Linne (Gaelic) – pond

Mactalla (Gaelic) – echo

Molag (Gaelic) – pebble

Nae (Scots) – no, not any

Noo (Scots) – now

Oriole (Latin) – golden

Peely wally (Scots) – sickly

Rionnag (Gaelic) – star

Salaan (Gaelic) – salt

Saorsa (Gaelic) – liberty, and freedom

Scran (Scots) – food

Snollygoster (19th-century English) – shrewd and dishonest person or a crooked politician

Tioram (Gaelic) – dry

Tonn (Gaelic) – wave

Torc (Gaelic) – boar

Tunnag (Gaelic) – duck

Wee (Scots) – small

Yaldi (Scots) – hooray

Ye (Scots) – you

Ye'sel' (Scots) – yourself

AUTHOR'S NOTE

The moon is 400 times smaller than the sun, yet on certain days and at certain times it blocks out its light and warmth to the inhabitants of the earth. As humans, we are intelligent enough to know that such an eclipse is a momentary event and that the sun will cast its light and warm us once again. But what happens when darkness casts a shadow on life and we forget that it's an eclipse? What happens when darkness appears greater than light? This is a story for children of every age, for we are all in the same boat, needing hope as much as oxygen.

INTRODUCTION

This story is a book about a book and the folk to whom it belonged. The *actual* book is called *The Legend of Ardnamurchan*, a very ancient and magic chronicle of great importance that belonged to the silkies.

The silkies are mythical creatures that live around the shores of the Ardnamurchan, a long finger of land surrounded by water on the west coast of the Highlands of Scotland. The silkies recorded their stories in *The Legend of Ardnamurchan*, or *The Legend* for short.

The silkie is a man on the land and a seal in the sea. In their human form, they are tall and beautiful with long, silky raven hair and their eyes (which are larger than those of humans) are like pools of black ink. There is so much to know about the silkies, but the people on the land only knew (through fables and suchlike) about their heroic deeds, especially their rescue of humans in danger at sea.

Years ago, many more Scots than today believed in their existence, even if they had never seen them. The whole belief system was similar to that of angels, in so far as a lot of people accept that angels exist, even if they have never seen one. Additionally, most agree that angels help people in need and, if they appear at all, it is fleeting. Angels soon disappear once their task is completed. And, generally, people thought of silkies in the same way, although they called them the seal folk.

But the waters of silkie folklore were muddied with the advance of modern times and scientific thinking. Silkies were unofficially reclassified as 'the mythology of the ancestors' and packed off to fairyland where all make-believe things go. Yet, contrary to expectations, the mythical creatures didn't go to fairyland: instead, ashamed of their imaginary status, they retreated behind a veil to live in virtual anonymity, where they remained unseen, but not unreal.

Their home was Seal Island, a wild and far-away place with an automated lighthouse that stood on a colossal mass of moody black rock that had been carved out over thousands of years into giant bottomless cauldrons that erupted every few seconds with explosions of water from the sea below. About four times a year (weather permitting), a lighthouse inspector visited the island in a small motorboat, that he moored on a nearby wooden pontoon. Whenever the officer checked over the lighthouse he found it well cared for and in good condition with no need of repair. Being an Ardnamurchan man, he knew that the 'seal people' took care of it, and so it was his custom to leave them a basket of homemade gifts: marmalade, shortbread and oatcakes. The silkies repaid his kindness by returning the basket filled with fish and shellfish, which they left just inside the lighthouse door. And for now, this was the only contact that the silkies had with the human world. The inspector didn't venture into the island's interior (nor did he tell anyone about its inhabitants) and the silkies made themselves scarce during his visits.

Eventually, however, something did happen. The banished creatures – that is, the silkies, and some others called the sea hounds – returned from 'behind the veil' and united with the land folk (as they called them) to do something pure-dead-brilliant that healed the land.

LEGEND HOUSE AND MACTALLA

In the heart of Seal Island there was a deep valley, an evergreen forested biosphere, and within the heart of the valley was a vale, a clearing where there stood a large, round, wooden building with a thatched roof. Inside was an outer ring, a curved gallery from where one could look down on an arena.

At the arena's centre was a firepit surrounded by wooden benches. This was Legend House, where the silkies gathered to meet, eat together, tell stories and sing songs.

But above all, Legend House was home to their greatest, most treasured possession, the *Legend of Ardnamurchan*. This was their sacred book of origins and history, of songs and wise sayings.

The Legend was ancient and heavy with front and back covers held together by an exquisitely carved gold clasp. The binding was of a beautiful and mysterious leather that had been artistically folded and shaped into swirling patterns that portrayed the winds of the earth on the top half of the book and the waves of the sea at the bottom. An eagle crafted from pure gold dominated the upper cover. One of his magnificent wings swept across the top of the book whilst the other flanked its spine. His eyes were fixed on a large fish that swam in the waters on the lower half of the cover, and with open talons, he was ready to seize it. Near the fish, a sea hound swam in a leather-creased kelp forest and above the water a silkie reclined on a rock.

Unlike those history books that fill the shelves of school libraries and contain dry toast-without-butter facts and figures about past events, *The Legend* was a living treasury of stories that travelled through time from a different age and a different place and came to life before the audience.

When the reader spoke the written words, they rose from the page to become three-dimensional living words. But in no time at all, they entered a fourth dimension, where they changed again into portals, doorways into the worlds that they described. These worlds were literal, such as a place in the countryside or a city, an underwater realm or a mountainous region.

And as the narrator spoke, the listeners passed through into a fifth dimension where they were transported into the realm of the story as if it were real-time, and as if they were a part of it, experiencing all its sights, sounds and even smells. This was *The Legend of Ardnamurchan*. The silkies believed that the book was kept alive through firstly public recitals in their gatherings, and secondly the updates of important new stories. Some silkies even foretold that the end of the book would be the end of the silkies, but others supposed this was only a superstition. Long before, only one human, an accidental visitor to Seal House, had ever heard a reading of *The Legend* and her experience was so life-changing that she left the land of men to become a silkie. After that, the silkies ruled against land folk attending the recitals, in case any more should fall under the enchantment of the sea.

One evening, no different to any other, the family gathered in the clearing in front of Seal House. It was a festive summer night and everything blushed softly orange in the light of the lanterns that hung from the trees. The delicious aroma of roasted fish infused the air and the melodic rhythm of dimdim drums worked their magic. It was a jamboree and everyone was lost in the dreamlike quality of the evening.

A feast was always followed by a reading from *The Legend* and tonight Mactalla arose before the assembly. Their leader, he was a tall man with a round seal-like head and long, dark, reed-like hair. His cheeks, like orange peel, were pitted and covered in short, stubbly whiskers and his dark eyes were pools of kindness.

The enchanted air that hung around the book made Mactalla's fingers tingle as he unfastened the golden clasp. The reading for that evening was from Book 1, Chapter 5: The Sons of Great North.

As Mactalla uttered the first words, the whole community was whisked by an irresistible force into another world and things started to happen. They found themselves in a fishing harbour where the first sensation to meet them was a draught of salty air and the cackling of fickle seagulls that billowed in the breeze like flotsam and jetsam; their squawks also were scattered to the winds and heard in other places, quite detached from their owners. A fisherman's dog, a Jack Russell (who wore a neckerchief and looked not unlike his owner) was harassed by the pesky birds, and barked incessantly at the air above his head. Aromas of freshly baked bread and roasted clams wafted down the quayside and mingled with funky fumes from yesterday's fish market – the juice of which had stagnated between cobblestones – and a pile of grassy horse dung that steamed against a wooden barrel. But soon the spectators were plunged into an underwater marine-scape as Mactalla narrated:

'Land folk say that the Northern Ocean is a vast sea, but we call him Great North. The smallest fish to the greatest leviathan live in him, and every creature in between. They resemble pipes, horses, angels or parrots. Still others mimic plants, sand or stones. Then there are those that light up the depths or hide in their own grotesquery.'

For anyone who knows what it is like to walk through a tunnel under an aquarium, with fish swimming all around, this was infinitely more profound, for this was a journey into the heart of Great North, who was too vast to be seen. In this place one could only be a drop in the ocean of his presence and marvel at his handiwork. And even so, these things can hardly be told, only experienced.

Mactalla continued.

'Great North has many seas: some are a frozen winter wonderland, others are a green turbulent fury and still others are a playground for dancing dolphins. Coral gardens of pastel shades host shoals of prettily painted fish and the moody octopus. Some places are too deep to be visited and remain unseen, except by Great North, who cherished them in his heart.

'The blue whale, the largest of all animals, can travel all her days in Great North, yet her paths remain unknown. Great North is too deep and too wide to understand and so too are these mysteries.

'But, in the beginning, when Great North was younger than today, he was surrounded only by himself and he had no offspring. The abyss of his heart opened and life came forth: jellyfish and eel, salmon and trout, lobster and crab, cod and stingray. But these creatures were simple and had no understanding or knowledge of their creator. Great North longed for sons, for surely he would carry them on sea currents and they would explore the deep and beautiful places within him; he would teach them the ancient wisdom of the sea and show them his treasures. And sons would help him to govern and rule.

'Great North regarded the seals and from a place deep within his oceanic being, something stirred. From among their number, he called some to be sons and they became silkies with knowledge of their creator. Corran was one chosen and Great North taught him songs and the wisdom of the sea. One day, when Corran saw the land of Ardnamurchan, his heart desired to explore it. So, Great North gave Corran the ability to become like one of the land folk, and to speak their language. He set before him an invisible bridge that no ordinary seal could see, for silkies were given supernatural vision to see the unseen crossing and go back and forth as they pleased. The land folk called them the seal people because they were men on the land and seals in the sea. The bridge was also the place where, one day, at the end of his life, a silkie would cross over for the last time and so forever lose his ability to become a man.

'Great North appointed Corran to watch over the

seas and help the land folk. He became Corran the Galad and spent many years in human form, living on the land, because there was a great deal of work to do; the land folk were poor and needy and the clan chieftains fought amongst themselves – which made everyone poorer still. When Corran the Galad was nearing the end of his life, he heard Great North calling him home. But before he crossed the bridge for the last time, he prepared the land of Ardnamurchan for his leaving. First, he appointed his son, Gull, as leader of the silkies; he and his descendants were the Galaidean (or the noble guardians) of the sea. Gull was the first in a long line of wise Galaideans, who lived, worked and held assemblies on Seal Island.

'Corran also appointed Tonn, a brave and worthy otter, to whom he likewise gave the gift of knowledge and speech, and he was no longer an otter but a sea hound. Tonn was the father of the river Galaidean.

'Cloud, a golden eagle and her kind, became sky hunters. Corran gave her authority to rule over the winged creatures and the sky's domain. She and her descendants were the sky Galaidean and met together on Corran's Mount. It was the sacred place on the land of the Ardnamurchan where Corran had first chosen and appointed the silkies, the sea hounds and the sky hunters to guard sea, shore and sky and to bring help to all in need.'

. . .

LIFE ON EARTH as we know it is chronologically ordered into a sequence of events; a timeline that has a beginning and an end with our own lives positioned somewhere on it, but when *The Legend* was opened and read, the timeline, like a tethered bird set free, took flight to go where it pleased. This was the ancient wisdom of the sea, and generally unknown to the land folk.

The next morning, Mactalla made his way to the lighthouse, a place he had frequented since becoming leader of the silkies, but the reasons for his visits were to do with the death of his father, Tunnag. When he was only a boy-cub, a seal hunter had killed his father for his skin. The seal hunter, who came from a foreign land, had never heard of the silkies, and he knew no better. Even so, killing seals for their skin was against the law in this country. For that reason, to slaughter an ordinary seal is bad enough, but to kill a silkie is akin to murder.

Mactalla grieved deeply, but in time, as leader of the silkies, he used the automatic lighthouse (on the side of Seal Island that faced the open sea) as a lookout tower to watch for seal hunters. And on this morning, sensing the need to go to the lighthouse, he walked through the forest along the pine-needle path towards the coast.

When a silkie nears the end of his life, he bequeaths his skin to a *chosen other* for it to be made into a coat. This parting gift is more than just a skin; it is the conveyance of a silkie's soul, containing the good things from his life and character. Whenever a human has come into the possession of a silkie coat, either by accident or if they have received it as a gift, the garment has worked a strange power on them, so much so that those who had a bad or flawed character before went on to live a good life. And, if they were good before, they went on to live an exceptional life.

Mactalla's coat had been given to him by his uncle Torc, who wanted to honour the memory of his brother and in some way to provide for his son.

As Mactalla mused on these things, he emerged from the calm green tranquility of the woods onto the shore with its expanse of watery sky, crashing surf and black jaggedy rock. With a strength and ease beyond that of humans, he strode across the boulders, a dark silhouette against a wall of white sea spray, the tails of his long leather coat flying in all directions like a wind-whipped kite.

Inside the lighthouse, out of the wind, he caught his breath, climbed the steps to the top and settled into his watch. Later that day, he spotted the outline of a great eagle rounding the coastline towards the lighthouse. The huge expanse of his powerful wings was steady and unbuffeted by the offshore wind as he made straight for the lighthouse. This was the great leader of the sky hunters, who lived on the Ardnamurchan and held council on Corran's Mount. Tioram had never before visited Seal Island; why was he here now?

Mactalla descended the lighthouse steps two at a time to meet the great eagle. They met away from the deafening surf; their foreheads touched in a greeting.

'Friend, I have news of Oriole.' The sound of Tioram's rich and golden voice rippled through Mactalla's soul – not only because of its deep resonance, but also because of the name he spoke. Mactalla stared unblinkingly at Tioram, and waited for him to continue.

ORIOLE

Oriole was an illustrious and resplendent bird, a winged prophet. No other creature in the land of the Ardnamurchan had beauty to compare with hers; her head, body and wings were a kaleidoscope of shimmering golden hues. The long train of her tail feathers was a dazzling array of swirling patterns and stripes in jewelled colours. Her flight left a rainbow trail in the sky, and because of this, the land folk called her 'the rainbow bird'.

Her main food was golden waxberries that grew on small bushes around the shore of a very remote, high-altitude mountain loch. It was the proximity of the bushes to the sun that made their fruit unusual, for they drew energy not only from the rays above, but also from the sun's reflection on the water below. Their flavour was not dissimilar to strong, dark honey (the Greek kind) whilst their texture was like softened wax and at their core were tiny seeds of living gold. These berries gave Oriole her rainbow-coloured iridescence, but most importantly, the property of the wax coated her feathers with a thin protective shield that kept her safe from the pollution of fear and despair, for she was a winged prophet of hope.

People are born with the light of hope in their hearts, but the strong winds of adversity can extinguish its flame, and then, in a darkened state, the heart becomes a graveyard of dreams, haunted by spectres of fear and despair that foretell of doom from the shadowy ruins within. This is not how humans are meant to be: it is how they become. For such as these, Oriole sang destiny songs that were bestowed in flight as she circled above them – and extraordinary things happened: their worlds of grey were transformed to colour and their long dark nights of despair were eclipsed by the light of dawn. Then there were men and women whose plans were to do something good or great and over them she released a supernatural power for success.

But Oriole was missing. Some land folk thought she had died, whilst others gloomily predicted that the general wickedness of people had driven her away. Hopelessness had settled on the Ardnamurchan like thick layers of ash; it felt as though it would seep into your skin, enter your bones and turn you grey from the inside out. Businesses closed, men lost their jobs and hung around the pub where they bickered and brawled and looked for answers in a jug of beer.

Women worked their fingers to the bone. It was a land of mouldy wheat, stinking tatties and maggoty cabbages. All were affected, young and old – from peely wally children, all pinched and pale; to weathered grannies with chocolate raisin eyes who gazed at the fire, lamenting that things had never been so bad, not since the war, but that was not so bad, because then people had hope whereas now, they had none.

Tioram spoke again.

'Aye, we know where Oriole is.' Then, leaning forward, he said gravely, 'She is on Storm Island.'

A troubled and forbidding place, Storm Island hid in dark cloud that clung to the island like a crowd of resident ghosts. The surrounding waters were a maelstrom of snake-like currents, dangerous riptides and hidden rocks that together formed a forbidding moat around a stronghold. On an unexpected fair-weather day, a yachtsman might chance upon the island, but local folk stayed away – and the weather and tide were not the main reasons for their avoidance.

'Ye mean…Arioch…?' said Mactalla, staring hard at Tioram.

ARIOCH

remlin is the proper word to describe a creature like Arioch, but you could also say he was a hobgoblin. These days, the words *gremlin* and *hobgoblin* conjure up images of ghouls in computer games or even mischievous imps in a fairy tale. Those portrayals are feeble compared to the entity of Arioch. He was a real, live, dangerously evil hobgoblin, made all the more dangerous because none of the land folk on the Ardnamurchan really believed in his existence, let alone his capacity for evil.

His wiry body was bogging-filthy and covered with red, leathery skin criss-crossed all over with old, white scars. A kilt hung on his torso, so grimy and tattered that it was impossible to tell its original colour or pattern. His rhinoceros-skin hands were toughened by years of cold, rough living and his heart, like his hands, was callous and unfeeling. But his gargoyle face crowned his unimaginable ugliness, and through the window of his skeletal eyes one could see the deplorable horrors of his soul within.

He lived in an almost inaccessible cave, high up in a rocky cliff that overlooked one of the beaches. His only occupation was theft; whatever he craved, he fixed his mind on it until he had hatched a plan to steal it. In this way, Arioch had once taken possession of Storm Island and had now lived there for so long that he believed it had always belonged to him.

On the odd occasion sailing folk dropped anchor to explore, Arioch unleashed an arsenal of attacks to oust them. Invisible in shadows, he ambushed hikers on narrow mountain paths by shoving them off the cliffside. Noise, however, was his chief weapon of terror. Like a multi-headed monster he projected a pandemonium of snarls, shrieks and blood-curdling howls that charged the atmosphere with unimaginable terror. His voices were all the more spine-chilling because of their apparent detachment from any owner; like a demonic ventriloquist, Arioch sent his unearthly cries into the air and like tormented ghosts they went in search of people to haunt. It filled him with grotesque glee to see his horror-stricken victims hurtle down the mountainside to escape the island as fast as their failing jellified legs would carry them. But they were the lucky ones – the psychological impact of his tyranny often caused paralysis in his prey – who became sitting ducks for his stone missiles, fired so adeptly from his slingshot that even in fog, he never missed.

Despite the known presence of a sinister hostility on the island, the Ardnamurchan folk had never seen Arioch, since he possessed an uncanny ability to fade into shadow and rocks, so they speculated on such possibilities as bogles or a restless and revengeful ghost of an ancient clan chief. The Galaidean knew that Arioch was real, however, and they had tried on many occasions to remove him, but even in good weather when reaching the island might be possible, finding Arioch was impossible, since his knack for detecting the presence of 'enemies' was practically supernatural. And, in sensing danger, Arioch could retreat inside the labyrinth of the mountain for long periods of time. As a result, the Galaidean had given up trying and the local folks simply stayed away.

'We should have dealt with Arioch a long time ago,' Tioram confessed, 'and now Oriole is suffering. The land is suffering. I am to be blamed for not leading in the way of a true galad.'

'Och! Ye are not the *only* galad!' cried Mactalla. 'Peace, Tioram! Arioch is building his own gallows. Justice will lead to victory and Oriole will be saved. She will rise on wings again.' Mactalla's words were strangely hopeful and Tioram felt confidence return.

'But Tioram, how do ye know that she is on Storm Island?' asked Mactalla.

'Och!' said Tioram. 'In two days, the council will gather on Corran's Mount and we'll talk about it then. Can you brief the sea hounds? I'll notify the sky hunters. Speed the falcon is awaiting orders.' And with that, Tioram was gone.

There was nothing for Mactalla to do, but wait for the morning, find the sea hounds and then make his way to Corran's Mount. And for now, as dusk approached, another evening at Seal House beckoned.

As he wandered into the clearing, the air was filled with the sweet and silvery notes of the Jali, one of the silkie's most important instruments, a wooden six-stringed lute, beautifully carved and inlaid with shell. Three musicians sat on tree stumps, with their legs astride the Jali, which they plucked like harps. Every chord was flawlessly timed and like an exquisitely choreographed dance their voices seemed to weave in and out of each other's to perfection. They were singing *The Seal Mother* and Mactalla stopped to listen, sipping his sweet and salty seaweed beer from a wooden cup. Everyone was in high spirits. If only they knew about Oriole.

That evening they ate fish wrapped in leaves and

smoked on a wood-fire, to the sounds of the Jali and the dim-dim drum. In the clearing aglow with orange light, night birds sang in the forest trees and cubs frolicked, the sound of their play only adding to the music.

Later, inside Seal House, Mactalla opened *The Legend* before an expectant audience. Prompted by listening to the song of the Jali players, he opened Volume II, Chapter 7, to the story of Shona, the seal mother.

SHONA, THE SEAL MOTHER

'This is the story of Shona, the silkie who became a seal mother to twins, a boy and a girl, whose parents tragically died in a storm. Before that terrible day, the family lived happily on the coast in a wee cottage with a thatched roof. One day, however, as the father was fishing in his boat, black clouds bunched together and struck the bay like the fist of an angry giant.'

As Mactalla spoke in the cosy fire-lit house, a storm appeared before their eyes and one of the cubs shivered when a trickle of ice-cold air ran down his back. Mactalla paused as the magic began to work its spell; there were sound effects as the god of thunder split the sea with his lightning rod and roused a monster from the deep. As the leviathan ascended, its gigantic gargoyle head towered above the waves whilst its huge tail thrashed the turbulent sea. It opened its fiendish mouth to roar and slime drooled from between multiple rows of razor-sharp teeth. Mactalla continued:

'The mother wrapped herself against the cold and battled her way to the shoreline to look for signs of her husband. Out of the howling black night the frozen rain, like tiny bullets, peppered her face and blinded her eyes but even so, she caught a fleeting glimpse of her husband's boat as it reeled and wrecked on the rocks.

'In a rash moment of foolish bravery, she threw herself into the surf with the hope of rescuing him, but little did she know that the sea had already claimed his life and she was about to meet him in the watery grave.

'Shona found two small children alone in the cottage; their names were Logan and Isla and she adopted them. The villagers knew that she was one of the "seal folk", and so they accepted her, for they knew she was good. They also knew that seal folk only come when they are needed – and these children needed a mother. However, they never spoke of her silkie nature in her presence, for this would have been impolite.

'When Shona disappeared, her silkie family went looking for her and were surprised to find her sea-changed and living like one of the land folk. They longed for her return, but when they saw the grace and beauty of her human form and her ardent love for her new wards, they recalled the words of an aged seer and remembered that this was her true fate. For when Shona was younger, an old and wise silkie had foretold her destiny that she would one day have children, but not of her own flesh and blood. It was evident to all that the discovery of the twins was the fulfilment of prophecy.

'So Shona became a part of village life and greatly contributed to the overall prosperity of the neighbourhood. To generate an income, she raised chickens to sell eggs and with the earnings she bought a sewing machine. Silkies are intelligent, quick to learn and capable, so before long she earned a reputation as the finest dressmaker in the region and attracted customers from afar. Soon the town began to flourish and prosper.

'She was a black-eyed beauty with hair that shone like pure coal and tumbled down her back in waves. Men were attracted to her like bees to honey – some even travelled from other villages just to see her – and over the years many fell in love with her, but she refused every proposal on the grounds that her devotion was only for her children.

'In the evenings, around a warm and cheery fire, Shona taught Logan and Isla the *Songs of the Sea*, and for the rest of their lives the twins would never hear any other music to compare with the haunting melancholic beauty of their mother's rhapsodies. The ballads conveyed the ancient lore and wisdom of silkies, and since this was otherwise unknown to land folk, the children became wise beyond their age and as they grew older, their counsel was sought by many.

'From time to time, the children caught Shona gazing at the horizon with a wild and faraway glint in her eyes, but when she sensed them watching, she smiled and withdrew from her private reverie, busying herself with household chores. There were places in her heart that even they did not know.

'Finally, there came the day of the twins' eighteenth birthday. The seal-mother had ensured that they were well educated and skilled; Isla was a dressmaker like her mother and Logan was a fisherman. During supper, Shona made them promise to care for each other and later, as she kissed them goodnight she relayed the proverb that she had told them every day since that first day of their adoption. "Remember...there is a place where sea meets land and truth meets legend."

'At dawn, whilst the twins slept, Shona returned to her home in the sea. In all her years as a dressmaker, she had sewn many fine clothes, but on her departure she took a single garment that she counted as the most beautiful of all; the villagers had never seen her wear it although it was her greatest possession. It was her silkie skin.

'Logan and Isla never forgot her words. In time, they found partners and the two couples stayed in the bay and built a second cottage where they lived as neighbours and had children of their own. The cousins spent their days playing pirates on the sugary sands and chasing crabs. Once in a while, a lone seal would appear and watch them from a distance before disappearing into the water.'

AFTER THE STORY, Mactalla thought for a long time about Shona and the courage that had led her to live among the land folk. As magical as *The Legend* was, and as vividly as the stories came to life before them, Mactalla felt the weight of history on him. He considered the greatness of his ancestors and wondered if such things could ever happen again, and if he himself would ever make it into these pages.

JETTE AND REEF

J ette's father, Salann, was the leader of the sea
hounds; in his youth, he had been a strong
warrior, but now, in his autumn years, his
daughter assumed his duties on his behalf.

If the land folk had forgotten about the existence of
silkies, they had completely forgotten about their much
shyer cousins, the sea hounds. Curiously, the name
Ardnamurchan in the Old Scots language was thought
by some to mean *the Land of the Sea Hounds* – an ancient
way of saying *the Land of the Otters*. It is true that otters
have always lived in the Ardnamurchan, and that sea
hounds bear some small resemblance to *giant* otters –
at least when they are at sea – but they are not the
same. For, like silkies, sea hounds possess the power of
sea-change. They have been described by

Ardnamurchan folk (who occasionally spotted them, usually from a distance) as '*grrreat* big dogs, uncannily bonny – no doubt about it – in fact, drop-dead gorgeous...' or words to that effect.

In truth, even the most 'gorgeous' regular dogs pale into insignificance next to these majestically resplendent creatures, and to see them at close range is to understand the difference between their intelligence and that of common animals. Their long and glossy fur varies in colour from one to another: some are black and shiny, others are bespeckled with silver and grey, whilst still others are a hundred shades of pebbly beach. They run like the jaguar, virtually gliding through the air, only lightly touching down between bounds, with fur that ripples like barley in the wind.

Jette and Reef's playground was a subterranean forest, a place where kelp trees stretched impossibly from the ocean bed to the surface and swayed in the endless rhythm of the sea, a place where the warm fingers of the sun made the underwater jungle flicker with emerald light. Their favourite place to fish was on the shores of Eagle Island. Sea hounds eat scallops, and hunt them like cats chasing mice. Clams try to escape by frantically opening and shutting their fan-shaped shells, like disembodied chattering mouths. They don't escape the belly of a sea hound, nor do crabs (another delicious meat), no matter how vigorously *they* scurry and scuttle for cover.

In his seal form, Mactalla swam to Eagle Island. Silkies and sea hounds make the sea-change through the crossing of a bridge; one that appears only when needed and only to the one for whom it is intended.[1] Some time later, he rounded the coast and walked towards the fishing bay.

Mactalla feasted his eyes on the island, all green and laden with dewdrops that sparkled as if someone had scattered thousands of diamonds instead of seed. Seagulls chorused whilst dipping and diving for fish in the turquoise surf and a lone seal (not a silkie) barked contentedly. How Oriole would love this, Mactalla thought.

With a tummy full of scallops, Reef lazed on a bed of dry springy seaweed and watched a flock of birds doodling shapes in the sky whilst Jette cleared up after their meal.

Coralee, the third member of their team, was moored in the bay. She was a magnificent sailboat with an emerald-green hull, polished wooden decks and a mainsail that bore the image of a golden bird which seemed to fly in the wind. A great shipwright and navigator had once built *Coralee*, pouring his spirit of adventure into her timbers. When, as an old man, he eventually died, the dreams of his yet unsailed voyages lived on in her.

When Reef and Jette found *Coralee*, the three pledged themselves to a life of valour, venture and voyage: they rescued drowning creatures from the thick black oil of tanker spills; they saved and nursed harbour seals wounded by boat propellers. The emergency services heard strange tales of the so-called angel dogs who came to the aid of holidaymakers: a family marooned on an islet by a fast incoming tide; a climber stranded on a rock face; hikers (no compass or map) lost in fog. One dark night, in icy rain, they followed the sound of distressed bleating to a small flock of half-frozen sheep clinging to a tiny patch of sodden ground in a flooded salt marsh, and herded them to the safety of a dry cave. Next morning, when the shepherd looked for his animals and found them safe and sound, he was flabbergasted that they were still alive. 'It's a miracle they survived, because ye know sheep!...Don't have the first clue in their silly heads. Not one clue amongst the lot of them!'

Mactalla ambled along the beach, unnoticed and beaming his famous smile as he watched his sea-hound friends.

'Jette and Reef!' he cried. 'I have found ye at last!' and flung open his huge embracing arms. In a very dog-like fashion, the hounds pounced on him, and he fell back on the sand in playful surrender. After the warm and cheery welcome, the mood changed as Mactalla gave news of Oriole and the council on Corran's Mount. The sea hounds nodded to each other in silent recognition and Reef turned his attention to the bay and beyond that, the horizon, to sniff the sea air and search it for reassurance, for wisdom, for anything. This was how he tried to make sense of the world – it's a sea-hound thing.

'Stay at Otterburn tonight,' said Jette, 'and tomorrow we'll go to Corran's Mount.'

OTTERBURN

O tterburn was the name given to the meeting house and council chamber of the sea-hound community. There was nothing to see of it from the land except a massive boulder that protruded out of the water, but below the surface, about two metres from the seabed, a gap in the rock led to a deep pool that surfaced inside a high-domed circular cave. A stone bench lined the inner wall of the round cavern, exquisitely carved with portrayals of sea hounds in heroic scenes of bravery and valour. The images ran along the backrest and were framed with wide panels that were equally splendid and just as intriguing: animals, birds and fish wove together in serpentine patterns; the sculpted creatures were so detailed and life-like Jette imagined that one particular stone trout would one day come alive and swim through the rest of the picture, and surely then, a nearby sea hound would give chase.

Most days, the community assembled at Otterburn to eat together. This evening, Reef, Jette and Mactalla dived down to the entrance of Otterburn and surfaced inside the cave. Molag and Linne, Jette's sisters, were cooking clams. Her nephews, a giggly ball of sea-hound pups, tumbled around their mother's feet, but as soon as they saw Mactalla, they wriggled out of the play fight and hurtled towards him in a race to be first to get in a story request.

'Mactalla!' piped Carran (who got there first), 'Mactalla! Can we have a story? Can you tell us the story of Salmon?'

'No!' squeaked Cu, Carran's brother. 'Cloud is more fun! Can we have Cloud, Mactalla?"

'We'll do both,' said Mactalla, chuckling at the merriment of the pups, who had become once more a whimsical knot of whiskers and tails.

Jette's father, Salaan, and other elders greeted Mactalla and took their places on the circular bench. Soon Otterburn was abuzz with clams-a-cooking, pups-a-playing, and the general banter of the day. Clams were no less of a feast for being an everyday food, for foods that are relished every day are a feast. Soon, a warm soupy cloud hung over the sea hounds as they savoured the supper, and the only sounds to be heard were the slurpings of clam-juice and the tinkling of empty shells tossed on a rubbish pile that grew higher and higher.

Later, Jette stretched her body before the warmth of the crackling fire and as she yawned, her long tigery whiskers glinted in the fiery orange light.

Mactalla was waiting in the centre of the cave to tell the sea hounds a tale from one of the carved pictures memorialised in their stone chair. Storytelling was in his blood, a gift passed down from his father, his grandfather and his silkie ancestors lost in time. In the unfolding of his tales, he pulled down a reality from the cloud of his imagination and in so doing, he transported his spellbound audience to another world. Just then, he cleared his throat and assumed a theatrical pose. Carran and Cu were lolling around on the ground, as young ones do, but when Mactalla made himself ready, they jolted upright and their whiskers twitched excitedly as they fixed eyes on the storyteller.

Mactalla began.

SEA-HOUND COVE

'One there was a sea hound called Salmon...
who lived with his family on a beach at
the far end of the Ardnamurchan. The bay
had a boring name up until that point,' he waved his
hand dismissively, 'but by the end of this story it was
called *Sea Hound Cove*. Life was happy and peaceful for
the sea hounds; they lived in the caves that lined the
shore and feasted on crabs and clams a'plenty.

'Things went on as usual, until one day land folk
arrived: a clan of men, women and children – battered,
bruised and confused. One of the land folk had a bloody
bandage on his head; whilst another with a broken leg
leant on a stick; the oldest and the youngest were
swooning with exhaustion. After a time languishing on

the beach, a party of young men went to search for firewood.

'From a distance, Salmon and the others watched the proceedings, and after some days, it became apparent that the land folk were there to stay, since they were busy gathering building materials. The sad arrivals trudged around in a shroud of gloom and Salmon watched them daily, curious to know more. Before long, he attracted the attention of a wee lassie.

'Sensing the wee gal's spirit of inquiry, Salmon appeared every morning at the far side of the bay on a large rock that jutted out of the water just a few metres from shore. And every day the wee gal went to visit the sea hound and they surveyed each other from their stations on the rock and the shore. Salmon noted the wee gal's observance of him: his much-larger-than-normal size, and his intelligence, which she seemed to understand was at least equal to that of her own.

'The following morning, she threw on her clothes skew-whiff and with blobs of porridge still around the edges of her mouth, she scrambled out of her shack and careered along the beach towards their usual spot. On her arrival, Salmon, who was waiting for her, folded his paws and bowed his head in a greeting.

'"Och, aye! I knew it!" she said. "They call me Fran."
'Salmon nodded.

'"Do ye want to know what we're doing here?"

'Salmon nodded again.

'This was her first encounter, since it had all happened, of kindness and *someone* who wanted to know her story.

'"The laird drove us off his land to make room for his sheep and me da says he'll make a pot of gold oot of it and nae bother with our pittance of a rent. The laird's thugs put us oot the hoose and burnt it. Da put his fists up and they took a stick and hit him on the head." Her face crumpled into a hot, red mess of tears and snot.

'"When I was a wee lassie," she spluttered, "the laird said we could stay if we put up hooses...and we did put up hooses...but he didnae keep his wud." Her report was considerably slowed by a fit of sobbing.

'"Da says, the lairds are devils," she blubbed. "They're putting folk oot their hooses all over the Ardnamurchan and then they're away to the Lowlands like softy southerners."

'Salmon urged her on.

'"We had wee hens, and a bubbly-jock and a veggie patch with tatties, but Mammy says the dirt here is boggin and ya cannae grow a thing. Da and the other men cannae fish and no one has a boat...Mammy's got a wee bairn in her belly and there's just a few oats left."

'Salmon turned to face the sea, but before disappearing into the water, he looked back at Fran and keenly stared into her eyes...and without him saying a word, she knew.

'"Haste ye back!" she cried in a scratchy voice as he slipped into the water.

'The next day, the sea hounds made their way to the newcomer's shanty town. Fran was buoyant with expectation. She had been trying to convince her dad and the other men to put off their hunting trip and stay, because, as she kept insisting, help was on the way. Embittered and bound by fear, the men only stared through her with defeated eyes and shuffled around getting ready to go. Fran was busy dodging and ducking her father's tellings off when suddenly a dozen or so sea hounds surfaced near the shore. She rushed to the water's edge, wildly waving her arms and beckoning the sea hounds closer whilst pogoing every which way like a demented flea.

'"Look, Da!" she squealed. "The sea hounds have come! They've come to help us!"

'"The wha...what?" said her father, who hurried to the shore in disbelief, only to see a myriad of fantastical creatures arrive and form a semi-circle near to the water's edge. Under the surface, between them and the shoreline was a long, dark, fluid shadow, a shoal of fish that they had corralled into the bay and were now driving towards the water's edge. Other sea hounds swam back and forth behind the herders to stop the fish from escaping.

'"Fetch baskets!" someone shouted.

'The whole village burst into action. Everyone grabbed a container. Before long the shallows were erupting with the flipping and flapping of hundreds of silvery heads and tails; even the children were scooping them into baskets. And sorrow gave way to smiles.

'Later that week, Salmon guided Fran along an embankment to an old, but sturdy, wooden boat that was buried under a pile of beach debris and with some repair it became the village pride. In the months that followed, the sea hounds coached their new apprentices where to sink lobster traps, lay nets, and so on. In time, Sea Hound Cove (for this was its new name) became a prosperous town, and its folk thrived at a time when many others were driven from their homes to either perish or set sail for the New World Colonies.'[1]

Otterburn erupted with cheering and barking and baying and the storymaster bowed low. Jette watched as her nephews dangled on Mactalla's arm.

Mactalla knew exactly what they wanted. He beamed and asked, 'Who was the most famous eagle of all: the mother of all the sky hunters?'

CLOUD AND THE KING

'Along time ago, a king's best friend was the eagle...and I'll tell ye why. In those olden days, kings were masters over their entire kingdom. The land folk, horses and dogs had no choice but to do his bidding; all obeyed and respected him, all except one.

'"The eagle!" piped one of the twins.

'"Carran! Shhhh!" said his mother.

'The eagle is not the servant of any master or king. A man may be a lord *or* a slave, but he will never tame or train the eagle, for she answers to no one.

'If a king wants to hunt with an eagle he must gain her trust and then, and only then, she might hunt *with* him, but she will never hunt *for* him. This is how he achieves it: when the eagle seizes her prey, she drops to the ground to kill it.

This is the exact moment when the king must take the eagle's catch, but if she sees him do it she will feel betrayed and her trust will be broken. So, in order to trick the eagle, he crawls on his hands and knees – most un-king-like – towards her and offers a gift of food. When the gift distracts her, he quickly takes her quarry and hides it under his cloak, since if she cannae see it she forgets that it is there. So, ye see, the king hoodwinks her into hunting *for* him, whilst cunningly keeping her trust.

'And so, because kings cannae make the eagle their servant, they make them their friends instead.

'In those days, there lived a great and powerful silkie called Corran the Galad. At that time, the land folk were dirt-poor and desperate, so he took on his human form and lived with them for years, performing miracles and doing good things among them. One day, Corran chose Cloud, a magnificent golden eagle, to be the mother of all the sky hunters. He bestowed on her the power of speech and intelligent thought and appointed her to guard the air and rule the winged creatures.

'But Corran had one other important task for Cloud. He wanted her to befriend the King, because, though he was a good man, and would make a good king, he was not yet strong enough to lead as a first among equals.

'For there were many clan chiefs in the Highlands of Scotland that scrapped over a patch of land like seagulls over a scrap of fish. These so-called kings presumed themselves to be *galad*, noble, but they didnae have the heart, mind or stomach of a king.

'The king was in need of loyal friends to help him rule wisely, yet he had a castle-full of servants whose lips dripped words of honey just to get his favour. And so it followed that Corran asked Cloud to help this special king.

'"Ye understand, my Lord," said Cloud, "that eagles serve nobody, not even a prince. But I am a sky hunter. How am I to enter the service of a king?"

"Ye will no' be his servant, Cloud, ye will be his friend," said Corran. "This king must rule over the land, but he cannae see it from the sky, as ye do, so tho' he has spies, I fear his enemies will strike before he is ready.

'"Cloud, ye have flight and speech and knowledge and the far sight of a sky hunter. You can be his eyes and his counsellor to make him strong."

"Does such a king live, my Lord?" said Cloud.

"Tomorrow, fly a sky hunter's half-day journey to Dunadd," said Corran, "to the royal mount where kings are made and on that hill there is a man's footprint in the rock.[1] Ye will see a prince place his foot in the stone: he's the one who will rule wisely and unite the land. Will ye be his friend?"

'At sunrise, Cloud flew to the Mount of Kings and soon after her arrival she saw a royal procession making their way to the hilltop. Leading them was a dark-bearded prince with a strong face. He wore a red cloak over his broad shoulders and carried a sword with a golden hilt. When he arrived at the footprint in the stone, he knelt in prayer and his courtiers, officials and princesses, with their ladies-in-waiting, did the same. Cloud flew to the rampart that surrounded the mount and observed from a distance.

'"My Lord," quivered one of the prince's subjects, "a golden eagle attends your ceremony."

'The courtiers were wide-eyed in wonder at her presence; it meant one thing and one thing only: a sign of divine favour.

'The prince was not astonished, for prior to the coronation, Corran the Galad had paid him a visit and made a promise to send him a friend, a confidante to help him govern wisely. The prince and the sky hunter regarded one another.

'"T'is a sign," the prince said. "This sky hunter will not be one of my servants, she will be my friend." He turned towards Cloud with a clenched hand on his breastplate.

"Our royal person is honoured," he said. "Welcome."

And Cloud bowed her head in response. The prince placed his foot into the stone, a symbol of his marriage to the land, and was proclaimed king.

'As the royal party travelled home, Cloud escorted them overhead. And from that time on, the King and the sky hunter were always together. She spied on his enemies, and overheard their plots as if she had been listening through walls of the thinnest paper, and in so doing, no ambush or scheme defeated her friend. In turn, he grew in strength and made the clan chiefs unite under his rule and established a peaceful kingdom aided by *his* friend, Cloud, the sky hunter.'

In Otterburn, the fire died away to embers and one by one, the sea hounds went to their beds, including Molag and her sleepy pups, whose dreams were filled with Salmon at Sea Hound Cove and Cloud, the King's friend.

CORRAN'S MOUNT

arly next morning, Mactalla and the sea hounds
began their journey to Corran's Mount. Their
first port of call was the bay of the Singing
Sands and as they set sail *Coralee*'s becalmed mood
shifted to action stations as she caught wind of the
mission.

"Valour!" shouted Reef, in the salty spray.

"Venture!" cried Jette.

"Voyage!" chimed in Mactalla, and *Coralee* plunged
deep into the sea, sending white horses racing along
her bow; the golden bird on her sail was once again
dancing in the wind.

The tranquil harbour of the Singing Sands came
into view and they moored close to the shore. Long
before (no one knows when), the land folk had given

the bay its name after hearing the curious glassy whine that the sand makes when it is being walked on. To their human ears, it sounded as though the sand was singing. Sea hounds and silkies, however, understood the sands, for it spoke in a real language, and on this day, it signalled that the beach was deserted, and therefore a safe and private place to undergo the sea-change, for this was one of the bays that they used to make the crossing.

Mactalla, already in his man form, began the ascent to Corran's Mount, knowing that Jette and Reef were soon to overtake him.

Sometime later, Reef emerged from the crossing in a coat that shimmered a thousand shades of gold. Jette was ahead of him, bounding through the hills towards Corran's Mount. She almost flew across the hill and her long black fur streamed in the wind like the mane of a galloping horse. She inhaled deep draughts of the honeyed mountain air and felt a surge of excitement, but it was not the aroma of the land that caused it: it was the smell of a mission. Nothing thrilled her more than a mission. A dangerous mission. A mission where solving problems was key. A risky mission. A rescue mission. A mission was life itself.

Corran's Mount was a slumbering mass of volcanic stone with grassy slopes that gave way to giant diagonal slabs of igneous rock. It was also the holy place where, in the dark ages, Corran the Galad had first given the sky hunters, the sea hounds and the silkies the power of speech and intelligent thought and appointed them to be the Galaidean, the Nobles of Ardnamurchan.

By now, Reef and Jette were far ahead of Mactalla and crossing a burn to join a narrow path that zigzagged all the way to the top. They leapt over streams that gushed and gurgled and whirled as they cascaded down to the lowlands; sometimes sounding hollow and cavernous as they disappeared underground. As the pair climbed higher the surrounding vista emerged, vast swathes of majestic undulating highlands, granite outcrops and beyond that, lochs that encompassed small pine-forested islands. They saw nothing else except birds or rodents flittering or scurrying on their way, but far above and out of their hearing range, sky hunters were heading straight for the mount.

As Reef and Jette arrived, Tioram, the leader of the sky hunters, was the first to greet them. He was perched on a large upright stone, the time-honoured seat of Cloud's descendants.

'Jette and Reef, welcome. Welcome to all. But where's Mactalla?'

'On his way...' panted Reef, as he bowed his head

and greeted everyone, who except for himself and Jette, were all sky hunters.

Yes, it was Mactalla's arrival everyone waited for; his presence both lighthearted, wild and free yet somehow weighted with the right kind of seriousness. His silkie wisdom, too, was greatly sought after.

Soon the mood became solemn as they awaited Tioram's address.

'Friends, we have news of Oriole.'

Only Tioram, Mactalla, and the sea hounds, that is, the Galaidean leaders, knew about Oriole and even they knew very little. From out of the stunned silence, questions started popping like corn in a pan.

'Where is she?'

'How is she?'

'When was she found?'

'Who found her?'

'Why did she disappear?'

And lastly, after an uncomfortable silence, Tioram answered the question that no one wanted to ask. 'Oriole is alive. Arioch has stolen her.'

'But how did ye find out, Tioram?' said Mactalla, bursting into the gathering.

'We have our trusted friend, Clamhan, to thank.'

All eyes rested on Clamhan, the buzzard, who modestly looked to the ground as they anticipated his report.

REFLECTION – FAILEAS

The local business folk of the Bay of Angels were developing the village and harbour as a holiday destination: new shops and a visitors' centre were soon to open. On the morning of Oriole's visit, the town was a hive of activity. The organiser of the event, in a flurry of decorative bunting and other party paraphernalia, flitted from one point to another with an endless stream of instructions.

'Take those tables to the sandwich tent, Angus.'

'Mary, show your dad where to put the chairs, there's a good lassie.'

'Ronah, do ye have the cheese and pickle ready?'

'Maggie, put the jam tarts next to the carrot cake.'

'Jimmy, take ye grubby mitts off those scones, the noo!'

In between running errands, children wearing homemade multi-coloured wings raced to and fro pretending to be 'the rainbow bird'. Haggis burgers and onions sizzled on a hotplate and several young boys hovered over them and got in the way of the portly cook.

'Skedaddle! Away with ye, laddies! They'll be done when they're done!' she squawked, and shooed them off with her spatula.

Inside the marquee, tables were piled high with a mouthwatering array of every kind of sandwich and cake. The celebrations began and everyone feasted. Some hairy-faced men in kilts sat together on a collection of tree stumps, blethering the day's gossip and sipping wee drams from their hip flasks. The soulful and resonant song of the bagpipe hung like a mist in the natural amphitheatre of the bay.

Later that day, Clamhan performed a flight display for the local people: a little girl held up a snippet of chicken and he zoomed in towards her, plucking it from her fingers before she realised he had taken it. She shrieked with delight while around her everyone laughed and applauded.

During the gala, Clamhan glanced across the Bay of Angels towards Castle House, a large white building with high turrets and towers that despite its name and appearance was not a fortress, but an inn.

The glass water of the bay reflected a mirror image of the house so perfectly that it captured his attention. As he briefly admired the view, he glimpsed something in his peripheral vision, something unknown that lurked around the foot of the inn. In the merriment of the day, he instantly dismissed the sight of it, although weeks later, when he was doing nothing in particular, the memory, like a forgotten dream, rushed back into his mind. The *unknown something* was not fully animal because it walked on two legs, and then again it was not human either, since it was somehow the wrong shape.

On that day of celebration, Oriole had stayed in a little turret at the top of Castle House as was her custom when visiting the Bay of Angels. It becomes apparent that this was the last time that anyone had recalled seeing her before she disappeared.

Later, Clamhan rekindled the mental image of the *unknown something*. 'Think, think,' he murmured to himself, 'it was wiry...and wasn't it reddish?' A horrible suspicion, like a demonic panther, stealthily crept into his mind and his feathers bristled. And it came with a hateful name. Now, he knew. The *unknown something* was Arioch.

Clamhan needed proof, so he waited for fog. When it finally came, early one morning, the Ardnamurchan was cocooned in a thick white cloud like a sleeping baby in a billowy shawl, so he ascended high above the fog into the clear blue sky and flew across the sea.

Storm Island is dominated, from one end to the other, by a saddle-shaped mountain with an unbroken ridge that runs along the top and slopes down on either side towards several beaches and bays. One side of the 'saddle' faces the north and the open sea, whilst the other overlooks the south and the land of Ardnamurchan.

Clamhan dropped down from the sky to the narrow ridge and then settled on a rock ledge whilst deciding his next move. He was inside a cloud that was drookit, heavy with dew, a perfect hiding place, since its wetness muffled noise. In this way, he advanced through the enveloping mist whilst scouting for signs of Arioch. It was a tightrope exercise of bravery and fear, and the odds seemed stacked against him: there was Arioch's sixth-sense of detecting so-called intruders on his island; there were his slingshot missiles of deadly accuracy even when they were projected in blind fog; and there was the likelihood that if he suspected espionage, he would move Oriole to a truly undiscoverable place.

After a long time, Clamhan heard a dull and distant sound of scree trickling down a slope; it seemed to come from the other side of the ridge. Rooted to the spot, he listened and waited, unsure of what to do next, but before long, much to his relief, something happened. From out of the mountain and the fog, there came a desperate faraway cry that despite its faintness pierced his heart like an arrow. 'Tioram!' it wailed. The voice, though broken and cracked, was Oriole's. She was located on the side of the mountain that faced the open sea, away from the Ardnamurchan. Clamhan ascended and joined the sky path back to the mainland. The following morning, he flew to Corran's Mount.

TIORAM WAS ALONE. The mountain air swirled around him in ribbons of pale sun and refreshingly chilly breeze. He breathed it in and felt strong. His sharp yellow eyes searched the horizon, for he knew in his feathers to expect a visitor. By and by, Tioram spotted a dark speck moving through the clouds towards him; shortly it became a smudge and finally it took the form of a sky hunter.

'Clamhan,' said Tioram, 'What news do ye bring?'

'...I have found Oriole,' he said, catching his breath. 'It was a difficult mission, my Lord.'

THE COUNCIL

'Justice finds a way,' reassured Mactalla, 'and in the council of many, there is wisdom.'

Whilst Ardnamurchan slept that moonless night, the company at the top of Corran's Mount hammered out their ideas around the fire. And in the wee small hours, a plan began to emerge. Two sites were chosen as suitable hideouts: Seal Ridge was a small rocky islet that jutted out of the water where ordinary seals (not silkies) lived. From here, a large portion of both sides of the saddle mountain could be seen. More importantly, it was the best position to monitor Arioch's cliff and beach. The second station was a tiny uninhabited wooded islet that overlooked the other end of the island.

There were drawbacks: as Tioram pointed out, on a

moonless or stormy night it would be impossible to see or hear anything. Also, cornering Arioch was useless since there was a labyrinth of interconnected caves inside the mountain, all of which were unmapped, but known to Arioch. Additionally, past attempts to lure Arioch away from the island, like a baited fish, had failed – and they had no reason to believe that this method would ever succeed.

Jette sat in silence, and in her mind she travelled along the Ardnamurchan coast that faced Storm Island, mentally exploring every bay, rock and shore in search of an answer. In the journey of her mind, she halted at the old, wrecked, fishing boat.

'That's it!' she proclaimed.

'What's it?' said Reef, and his whiskers twitched with curious excitement.

THE BLACK HOLE

(...AND HOW ARIOCH LEARNED OF ORIOLE'S WHEREABOUTS)

O ne day, when the weather was unusually fine around Storm Island, a family anchored their yacht in the main bay and went ashore. Arioch made his way down the rocky cliff towards a part of the beach where there were plenty of hiding places in between rocks and behind trees. Squatting inside the yawning mouth of a cave, he watched and listened. A clump of trees near the cave's entrance hid the rest of the beach from sight.

Two dungareed children, a young girl with a ponytail and a boy with a child's fishing net, ran ashore and hopped from stone to stone, exploring rock pools. With each hop, they moved closer to Arioch's hiding place. The brother and sister had stayed with their parents in the marina at the Bay of Angels, and they had made friends with local children who had told them all about the 'rainbow bird' and her up-and-coming visit to the village. Kneeling over a little rock pool, their heads close together, they prattled on whilst prodding a crab's pincer with a small twig to see if it would grip. The crab's stalky eyes surveyed the unknowable giants.

'Imagine if *our* eyes were stuck on the ends of stalks!' said the boy, and launched into an imitation of Jar Jar Binks, with arms, legs and tongue waggily flailing in all directions.

'Gross!' spat the girl, throwing her brother a look of irritation.

'How wude!' he retorted, but he quickly lost interest in the crab and its stalky eyes. 'Do ye think Mum and Dad would let us go back to the Bay of Angels and see the "rainbow bird?" It's only next Saturday.'

'Ben! Amy! Lunch!' cried a voice from further down the beach.

'Let's ask,' said Ben, and they hopped from rock to rock back to the picnic.

Arioch's blood simmered at the idea of folks being 'blessed' by the 'rainbow bird' and he hated them all the more.

An idea came to him: he would steal it. If it belonged to him, he would be successful all the time. 'No more scratching around for scran,' he muttered, rubbing his stomach. The more he thought about it, the more he convinced himself that the bird was an essential piece of property. In fact, it was meant for him all along. Once Arioch had fixed an idea in his mind, he could never unthink it, and now he would have to go through with it, or go mad, or die in the process.

Arioch grinned in self-congratulation over his genius brainwave and wondered why he had not conceived of it before. The wheels of his mind rotated slowly and then more manically as ideas whirled in his head about how he could accomplish the task.

The idea of kidnapping Oriole was a seed sown in his own selfish greed, but soon, like Jack's beanstalk, it spiralled out of his control. A magnetic vortex appeared before his eyes; it was a hellish black hole with a colossal appetite, and it was waiting to consume him. Arioch had no ability to defend himself. He had already given himself over to its power.

THE KIDNAPPING

A few days before Oriole visited the Bay of Angels, Arioch awoke on a night that was uncommonly still and as black as the Earl of Hell's waistcoat. He groped his way to a beach cave, dragged his coracle to the water's edge and followed the contour of the coastline towards the side of the island that faced a deserted bay on the Ardnamurchan coast. In the dead of night, the silence was only broken by the sound of water as it lapped against the side of the hull.

Sometime later, Arioch faintly perceived the black bulk of an old, rusty fishing boat that lay on the shore; this was the usual landing site for his occasional trips to the mainland. Pulling his coracle out of the water, he buried it, along with its paddle, under a large pile of washed-up seaweed in a gap between the side of the decayed vessel and the surrounding rocks.

He headed for the heights of Ben Rionnag, the place of a solitary lake where golden waxberry bushes grew around the water's edge. In the pitch-black, he fumbled on like a blind animal, falling foul of nettles and brambles in ditches. At the first light of dawn, in a barely visible, grey fuzzy world, his progress could have been faster, except for early risers and farmers on their way to work. It took him hours to move from tree to ditch and from hedge to hollow, and as the light increased, so did the number of out-and-about folk, which made his journey even slower. Nevertheless, by late afternoon he arrived at the foot of Ben Rionnag, and began to worm his way along an ascending zigzag path. With the onset of evening, he reached a narrow pass that took him directly to the secluded mountain lake and the bushes. Once there, he made a potion and dipped the waxberries into it, then he laid them out to dry. As daylight dimmed, he slugged whisky from his flask, swishing it around his chipped and rotten teeth and with heavy eyes, he fell asleep under a tree.

Arioch woke frowsily at the first light of dawn. The breath of his yawn polluted the air, and as he stretched his stiff joints, a withering stench wafted around him. He reached for his flask and quaffed his morning whisky before stowing the drugged berries in a tattered makeshift purse tied with twine.

For the rest of that day, he slunk down the mountain and crossed country in the general direction of the Bay of Angels. Nearing his destination, he buried himself in shrubby undergrowth and settled down for the night. As the big day dawned, he edged towards

Castle House, where he hid in the shadows until everyone had departed for the festival. With the agility and ease of a spider, Arioch ascended the hidden side of the tower, feeling his way steadily forward, fixing his fingers and toes in tiny crevices and on small bumps in the stonework. At the top, he hoisted himself over the ledge of the turret balcony and hid behind a collection of large, potted plants and a garden chair. The doors leading into the tower were wide open, so he slithered across the stone floor and peered inside the turret, then crawled down the polished wooden steps into the chamber.

The room was exquisite, filled with richly coloured wall hangings, two deep armchairs, a chaise lounge, and large, embroidered floor cushions. For all that, Arioch's ability to appreciate the beauty of something was narcissistically limited to whether or not he desired to own it. A thing was only beautiful if he deemed it beautiful, and he would only deem it beautiful if it was in his possession.

Atop a small round table were bowls made of olive-wood, filled with delicious morsels and sweetmeats: fresh dates, special roasted grains, toasted hazelnuts and golden waxberries, into which Arioch mixed his own.

When he had finished, he returned to his hiding place behind the chair and waited.

Early in the evening, Oriole flew to the balcony and settled on the stone ledge. Her iridescent train swished like folds of taffeta silk as she moved. She watched the sun, a ball of blazing fire, sizzle and melt into the ocean.

From behind the chair, Arioch's heart hammered so loudly he feared the 'rainbow bird' would hear it. As the light faded, Oriole fluttered into the turret and alighted on a wooden perch near the banquet. She took a waxberry in her claw and fell into the pleasure of the feast.

PRISONER

Oriole awoke on a mess of stale and dusty straw. A dreary shaft of light filled a nearby entrance. Bleary-eyed and senseless, she struggled to understand her surroundings; things were terribly wrong...but it was too difficult to think.

When her mind began to clear, she realised she was in a cave, but how was that even possible? She must be lost. But how could it be? Dread gripped her being. As she tried to move, she first realised that her body was stiff and sore, and secondly, that something jangled around her foot. She looked down to see a metal ring around her leg attached to a chain which, in turn, was fixed to the wall.

Kidnapped. The word stabbed her heart like a stone

dagger. As she struggled to make sense of it all, a noise from outside the gloom of the cave disturbed her.

The sound of Arioch's gravelly croak of pain was like the flick of a light switch and, all of a sudden, she realised what had happened. She had left the party at the Bay of Angels and flown to the tower. Whilst watching the sunset from the balcony, she had sensed a shadow, but in a moment of tiredness, she had ignored it. Her hostess had left a delicious spread of food, to which she helped herself. Then it seemed her body turned to lead and her brain melted into thick molasses. She knew she was about to fall, only a split second before it happened. Then there was nothing. Now, there was Arioch.

Oriole was relieved to identify her enemy. She was not a prisoner beyond rescue. The chain on her body would not become one on her mind.

Arioch squeezed through a gap in the rock. A trickle of dark blood oozed out of his knee and inched, like a black slug, down his leg. Seeing Oriole was awake, a grin, like a smear of dirt, spread across his face and his sinewy body twitched with feverous greed over his new possession.

Oriole's voice, normally so self-possessed, betrayed her trembling soul. 'What…have…ye…done?'

Arioch had been inwardly congratulating himself on the ownership of his new 'thing'. That a 'thing' could have a voice (and its own opinion) was an alien concept he instantly tossed aside.

'Ye have...taken me prisoner,' persisted Oriole, in her steadiest voice.

'Me got de rainbow off dem,' spat Arioch, angrily pointing towards the mainland. 'Me got de rainbow...' His voice trailed off as something else caught his attention: an old, dusty bottle of whisky lying askew on a stone ledge. He reached for it, wrenched out the cork with jagged teeth and spat it forcefully across the cave. He tipped his head back as far as it would go and slugged great gulps that moved down his neck in undulating bulges.

'Fire bru,' he grunted, rubbing his tummy and speaking to no one in particular. He quaffed the bottle again and growled.

Speaking slowly and deliberately, Oriole asked again. 'Why – have – ye – kidnapped – me?'

Her voice, though urgent, was distant and faint as though it came from miles away; it held no power to penetrate his inner fortress. It was of no consequence and demanded no answer. This thing had no expression of rights: it was his possession.

'The rainbow bird is mine now,' he muttered from his frozen oblivion. The thought of the 'rainbow bird' blessing 'dem land folks' made him squirm with loathing and disgust; he hated their existence beyond reason and restraint. His heart was a black hole of misery that greedily craved all other matter; it swallowed goodness, hope, joy and peace until nothing was left, aside from its devouring and consuming self.

'But without me they will die,' said Oriole.

'Die?' The word filled his mind with images of dead bodies and deserted houses in derelict villages and his eyes ignited with a diabolical black fire as he imagined the plundering. 'Och, they'll die!' cried Arioch, whisky spraying in all directions from between his crumbling, rotted teeth. 'Rainbow bird all mine now!'

Oriole asked him no more questions; she saw the truth: he existed in the centre of a world that was like a globe of mirrors with a thousand reflections of himself stretching to infinity. No room for anyone in this sphere, except those who slavishly served it.

Arioch was in his vast inner desertland, pacing back and forth as if searching for an answer. Suddenly, he was struck by an idea and, within a nano-second, his psyche rushed like a spectre from the far-off place inside himself to being fully present in the cave.

'All my days, I scratch around for scran,' he grumbled and thrusting his finger into Oriole's face, he bitterly demanded, 'ye do magic! And me eat so much, me belly bust.'

Oriole tilted her noble head towards him. 'As ye wish, Arioch. Bring me a sharpened stick.'[1]

He received her instruction as if she were a talking robot, and scampered away to find a wooden pole. Sometime later, he clambered back to the cave and presented the stick to Oriole, with a face that grimaced around the gaping hole that was his mouth.

'Find a place on the beach, in the shallows,' she said, 'and wedge the blunt end of your stick between two large rocks. Set it at an angle so that the sharp end points out of the water towards the sky. Leave it there overnight.'

Arioch scurried down to the shore, where he lodged the stick into place. Some hours later, he returned and fell on his bed, a stone ledge in a corner of the cave, made up of a sheep-fleece and an old, tartan blanket begrimed with grease and crud. Brooding over the stick, he drifted off to sleep.

At sunrise, Arioch scrambled down the cliff face to the beach and his eyes boggled at the sight of the miracle. Five fat fish were skewered on the stick, looking as though they had jumped out of the water to spear themselves! After cleaning them, he made a fire, gorged himself on roasted mackerel, and hung the leftovers to smoke. By evening, he crawled into bed, sated. 'Me eat so much, me belly bust,' he croaked, and five minutes later he was snoring. With every new day, there were more fish on the stick.

As days became weeks, Arioch spent more time on

the beach cooking, eating and smoking fish, and Oriole, in the absence of his vile presence, suffered a little less. Her prison was dreary and foul, but when Arioch wasn't there she could think and plan. During these times, she kept hope alive by thinking about everything that was the opposite of Arioch and her squalid jail. She mused over the long grass of summer that dies in the winter to become glitter-frosted sparklers in winter sun. She dreamt of the Bay of Angels with its deep, deep emerald loch and Ardnamurchan mornings drenched with drops of dew that hang like liquid crystal on every leaf and tree. But most of all she thought of her friends: Tioram, Clamhan, Jette, Reef, Molag, Mactalla and Speed, and sometimes feared they presumed her dead and other times trusted that they would not give up the search.

Arioch became lazy and as he continued to fill his belly, he occasionally forgot to guard the island. He also lost sight of the fact that the 'rainbow bird' was a prisoner, with friends who would be searching for her.

In his mind she was a 'thing' that he owned, not a living being with feelings and opinions or a need of thanks. She was the same as a food cupboard or a money bank that you go to for provisions.

Every day more fish. Other miracles, too. One day, Oriole told Arioch to leave the stick overnight amidst the branches of a wild fruit tree. The next day, the tree was full of juicy purple damsons. One day, Arioch wedged the stick in mountain rocks where he pointed it towards the sky and it caught wild birds instead of fish. On that occasion, it was a wet, indoors kind of day and Arioch returned to the cave where he busily plucked and prepared the birds for cooking. In one corner there was an open fireplace with a metal spit roaster under a rough hewn chimney. Arioch sat hunched over on a low stool, transfixed like a bug-eyed gargoyle by the rotation of the roasting birds as they hissed and crackled in the flames.

When Arioch remembered to feed her, Oriole ate honey and rough oatcakes. Days became weeks and weeks stretched to months. Only creatures or people that have been imprisoned can know how countless days and nights in captivity affect the body and mind. Time moves at a cold-bloodedly glacial pace, whilst the prisoner is tortured by the mind-numbing stagnation of it all, and just when the inertia reaches screaming point, the hours stretch agonisingly further.

During these times, Oriole's mind was gripped by a vice-like iron claw and gradually she lost the power of independent thought and reason. Delusions paraded before her eyes like different shades of a grey rainbow. She imagined the mountain was alive and the cave in which she was trapped was its throbbing, pulsating heart. The steady booming beat of the giant organ pounded her ears whilst the fleshy swollen walls almost suffocated her. Mirages came and went like visiting spectres: sometimes she watched the bird in the cave from somewhere outside of herself, as though it were a poor wretch in a story. The bird raged and then at other times it languished in misery, and whilst the scene was heart-breaking, Oriole's heart was frozen and she felt nothing for the caged victim. Still worse nightmares followed: hundreds of stone daggers came out of the walls and ceiling, pointing their blades towards her. She was a prisoner on trial and the daggers her accusers. They had condemned her to a lifetime of torture...but what was her crime? The daggers knew only that she was guilty. And whilst it was normally within Oriole's nature to fight such phantom terrors, she was under the power of another and losing all control. And then a dark shadow took up residence in her mind and though it never spoke, it conveyed a message that this cave-existence was her real life, whilst her previous one had been only a daydream. Lies replaced truth: grey rainbows were true signs of despair just as coloured rainbows were false signs of hope. And as in a nightmare, where absurd things become real, she accepted the lies as truths.

This continued day after day and she was losing her mind. But one day, the blinding fog that smothered her brain and controlled her thoughts cleared ever so slightly and she caught a pin-prick glimpse of reality:

Arioch's mind was like a black hole and it was sucking her by some kind of psychological-gravitational-force into its own world of misery.

'Tioram!' she screamed. The cry of his name was an arrow that went straight from her desperate heart to find the one she called. Arioch had gone to the waterfall.

THE PLAN

J ette sat quietly and mentally wandered along the coastline; she came to an abandoned, rusty, fishing boat on one of the isolated beaches that overlooked Storm Island. It reminded her of a time long ago, when a foreign merchant ship had crashed onto the rocky shore and lost its cargo of whisky. After that, the local inns and dwellings were well stocked. Sometime later, when invaders threatened the land, the locals put on a show of generosity by seducing them with liquor. In this way, they overpowered them.

'Ye know of the old ruined boat on the shore, opposite Storm Island?' Every head turned towards her.

'Remember the shipwreck that lost the kegs of whisky? Picture some fishermen in a boat. They have contraband, because they're not really fishing, they're *smugglers* bringing illegal goods into the country: crates of whisky. They head toward one of the trading islands, but on the way, they are hit by a violent storm. The men perish in a watery grave. The wind drives the boat towards Storm Island, where it capsizes on the rocks. Now imagine this: the boat smashes against the rocks and it sinks, but not before a crate of whisky tumbles onto the beach. The next day, after the storm has died down, Arioch makes a discovery.'

Mactalla's mind began to work; he'd heard of a forest woman living near the Bay of Angels who made herbal medicines; maybe she could prepare a drug to add to the bottles of whisky? Furthermore, the man who lived at Castle House ran a small whisky distillery; perhaps he would help? He thought of the storms that frequently hit the island. They would not have to wait long before putting their plan into action...and silkies have a special gift of predicting the weather; they can read the sea and sky better than any sailor can.

Mactalla addressed the company.

'Jette has a good plan, but we will have to change the way we do things...we need to work with the land folk.' Mactalla opened his huge arms and motioned to everyone present. 'Here *we* are! Silkies, sea hounds and sky hunters, and there *they* are, the land folk, but cannae ye see? Land and sea are joined together. Arioch is everyone's problem! The *us* and *them* must become the *we*. *Unity* brings justice to victory!' The truth of his words became truer as they were spoken. 'What do ye say about this?' Mactalla's gaze swept the counsel. In the past, silkies and sea hounds had not generally worked *with* land folk, they had only come to their rescue, and even then, anonymously. Many land folk believed in the 'seal people' (as they called them) and the sea hounds, but in a mystical kind of way. As with angels, faith and doubt were mixed concerning their existence. As for those very curious tales about 'seal people' living with land folk, such as Shona of the Sea or Corran the Great Galad, most had concluded they were just ancient fairy tales.

'Our brothers, the sky hunters, ye are not the stuff of myth: ye live in the Ardnamurchan and the land folk are used to seeing ye...even if they dinnae understand the full extent of your powers. Silkies and sea hounds live only in legend.' Mactalla leant toward their faces as he spoke. 'But it's time for the tide to turn,' he pressed. 'When waves run to the shore, they turn into seafoam... is that what we are? Seafoam?' His words began to grip their hearts. 'Shona said, "There is a place where sea meets land and truth meets legend." She didnae disappear on the sand like seafoam or like something out of a story book: she met the land with truth.'

Mactalla rose to his feet. 'I'm not afraid to stand before land folks and say:

I am a man upon the land,
I am a silkie in the sea.
We are sea folk of old,
To do the land good.'

The assembly erupted with bays, barks and cries of praise and approval, as all voted for change.

MAGGIE AND FERGUS

No one had ever heard of a silkie visiting a person's home. When Maggie and Fergus Doone first saw a tall, dark stranger in a full-length leather coat walking towards their house, they were struck by his appearance and stopped what they were doing to watch him approach. His stride bold and determined, he appeared fantastical against the everydayness of the landscape; his coat, clearly made of an animal skin, was of a kind Maggie had never seen before.

The Doones were practical people, but the sight of Mactalla drew them into an unaccountable knowledge that no less than destiny was walking towards them. At the local bar on a Friday night, ruddy-faced, pipe-smoking fishermen who wore thick woollen beanies and had their tongues loosened by wee drams, told tales of 'seal people'. Newcomers from the city, Maggie and Fergus assumed the stories were 'just a wee bit of Friday night fun', but now they found themselves on the threshold of discovery.

Fergus met Mactalla at the gate. 'Good day to ye, Sir,' said Fergus. 'To what do we owe the honour of your visit? I'm Fergus Doone.'

'Fergus, the honour is mine. I'm Mactalla,' he said, and the two shook hands. Half an hour later, Fergus, Maggie and the seal man were sitting around the kitchen table, bleached white from years of scrubbing, with steaming mugs of tea and Maggie's famous carrot cake. It was a triangle of fascination; the Doones could hardly believe they were hosting an extraordinary being in their very-ordinary kitchen. What's more, he was eating ordinary cake made from ordinary ingredients; Mactalla, likewise, was spellbound by the *extraordinary* Doone-folk and their extraordinary kitchen, crammed from ceiling to floor with delectable things. Around the walls ran a high shelf and hanging underneath it were hams and strings of onions, garlic, herbs and smoked sausages, as well as baskets of eggs and apples. On the countertops were copper saucepans, stacks of homemade preserves, some big cheeses and a ginger cat, which had plonked itself down in the only available space and now stared unblinkingly at Mactalla.

Mactalla wanted to stare unblinkingly at everything in the room, but checked his manners. He did, however, spy several bottles of Doone Whisky in a rack.

'Och, it's good to meet the both of ye,' Mactalla said, and beamed his winning smile. 'I've come about ye whisky.'

Fergus hesitated. Why was a 'seal person' asking him for whisky? Why was a seal person here at all, for that matter, let alone asking him for whisky? And absurdly, his mind flashed back to those fishermen at the pub who claimed the seal folk drank only seaweed beer.

'It's not for me, Fergus,' Mactalla said. 'It's for Arioch, on Storm Island.'

The Doones had heard conflicting rumours about a sinister presence on Storm Island. Some Ardnamurchans believed it was the troubled ghost of a Celtic king, whilst others claimed it was an evil spirit. Yet when Maggie heard the name 'Arioch' spoken out loud, fear dropped into the pit of her stomach like a heavy stone. Instinctively, she reached for the teapot, the down-to-earth reassuring cup of comfort in the face of ghoulish and unearthly things.

'What business do ye have with...it?' Fergus choked. 'I didnae think *it* was a creature...and how can my whisky help?'

'Fergus,' Mactalla replied. 'Arioch has Oriole.'

Maggie adored Oriole. She kept the little turret room at the top of the house for her visits. The heavy stone in her stomach grew in weight and size.

There was one last grievous thing that Mactalla had to tell them. Oriole had been in the turret when Arioch had kidnapped her. It was devastating news that knocked the axis of their world.

In the hour that followed, over more cups of tea, Mactalla, Fergus and Maggie discussed plans to rescue Oriole. Fergus packed six bottles of whisky into a wooden crate.

The two men, one from the land and one from the sea, were brothers in arms. Mactalla remembered Great North, who gave silkies the power to become men; to explore the Ardnamurchan and the world of people – to be friends and comrades – that must have been what he had always intended.

'I'm glad to be in a team with ye, Fergus,' said Mactalla.

'There's a saying we have,' said Fergus, cautiously. 'One ox can pull a thousand, but two can pull ten thousand.'

'Well,' said Mactalla, clapping his hands together, 'what about an ox and a seal?' And the warmth of shared laughter drained away the last of their shyness.

'Fergus, do ye know where we can get a boat?' said Mactalla. 'One that we can smash on the rocks?'

THAT OL' RUST BUCKET

Mactalla had never ridden in a car before. With one eye on the road, Fergus glanced sideways as Mactalla took in the new experience. People who walk everywhere see the world at that speed. Now as he sat in the car, the world whizzed by as he shot forward.

It was both exhilarating and disorientating – too much to see and too much rushing by. It helped if he closed his eyes, but then he didn't want to miss a thing.

They were on their way to see an old lady living in the Bay of Goats who had a ramshackle fishing boat sitting on her driveway. It had been there for years. People called her 'the goose lady' because she lived alone, except for her geese and other birds.

As they entered the goose lady's garden, the geese

reared themselves to their greatest size, hissing threateningly. With an outstretched palm, Mactalla commanded the birds to back down, and the geese reverse-waddled to let them pass. The man and the silkie continued to the house under the penetrating gaze of a few dozen beady eyes.

'Hullo, the hoose!' called Fergus through the slightly open door of a conservatory.

'Hi there folks, just coming.' A headscarfed woman appeared in a saggy, yellow cardigan with holes in it, and welly boots. In her village, Mrs Kelly was famous for two things: geese and wellies. The local folks joked that she wore her wellies in bed; the rumour had got around because no one had ever seen her out of them.

'What can I do for ye folks?' she said, peering out from under her headscarf. Mrs Kelly had sold duck eggs to Fergus before, and so she recognised him as a local, but as soon as she caught sight of Mactalla, her innards told her that he was one of the 'seal people'.

'How can I help ye, Sirs?' she said, casting a respectful glance at Mactalla.

'We are on a mission, Mrs Kelly,' said Fergus. 'Do ye want that old boat?' He pointed towards the driveway.

'Och, that ol' rust bucket? It was my Robert's fishing boat, but he has no' used it for years.'

'How much do ye want for it, Mrs Kelly?' Fergus asked.

Mrs Kelly looked from Fergus to Mactalla. It was clear to her that the 'seal man', who had already won her favour, needed the boat for some important reason.

'If my geese trust ye,' she declared, 'then so will I. Ye can have it.'

Mrs Kelly, squinting sideways at Fergus, said, 'Och, just buy some more eggs and we'll call it quits.'

'I'll take some back for Maggie,' said Fergus with a friendly grin.

Mactalla took hold of Mrs Kelly's hands and held them between his. 'Your gift will serve a great purpose, Mother.' Mrs Kelly felt strangely moved by his warmheartedness, since she was a lonely (and as she thought) unimportant woman with only geese for company. Misty-eyed, she managed a wobbly smile and blew her nose on a tissue. Mrs Kelly and the beady-eyed geese watched as Fergus and the 'seal man' hitched the little boat to the car and drove away.

AGNES FIFE AND THE ENCHANTED FOREST

North of the Bay of Angels was the so-called Enchanted Forest. It was so dense that even on bright sunny days, inside the forest remained a perpetual state of twilight. But there was nothing dull about it, for the forest floor was carpeted and the trees were covered in luminous green moss, which was partly why folk called it 'enchanted', although there was another reason: it was the home of Agnes Fife.

The local children fantasised that Agnes Fife was a witch and concocted stories about her making magic spells with toads and poisonous mushrooms. Her strange appearance fuelled their fertile imaginations. Her small brown face was pointed and wrinkly, and surrounded by a mass of scraggly white hair that stood on end like straw. She wore a long, old, leather coat that was scuffed and weather-beaten, just like her.

The adults didn't believe 'that silly nonsense' about Agnes being an enchantress and they mostly scolded the children for calling her so. Despite this, *they* shunned the old woman since they were afraid of what they didn't understand. In truth, she was just a forest woman who believed in herbal remedies and 'getting back to nature'. Her dwelling was a small log cabin with a grass turf roof that had ever so many bird feeders, wind chimes and jangly things dangling from the eaves over her veranda. The local children were spooked by the sound of the chimes, which convinced them all the more that she was a haggedy crone, but actually the house was not witch-like at all. It was just different. Her furniture, bowls, plates, cups and spoons were all hand carved from wood and she had running water in her cabin from an uphill stream. In winter it was cosy.

Mactalla climbed the steep pathway through the softly luminous forest towards Agnes's house. It was a long, winding path and the peaty forest air was fragrant with pine. Agnes was sitting on her veranda knitting when she spied Mactalla approaching her lodge.

'I know ye type,' she called out sourly. 'Ye are one of them "seal people". What do ye want?' She never opened a conversation with the usual polite greetings, but always said exactly what she was thinking.

'Madam, I have come for a cure.' His use of the word *cure* surprised her; she believed the forest held many cures, yet she was not about to trust a 'seal man', let alone one that asked her for a cure.

'Why would one of your kind come to a forest woman like me for medicine?'

'Nae, Madam, I dinnae need a cure for myself but a cure for this land,' said Mactalla.

'Ye have come to the wrong place. My remedies are for fevers, headaches and things like that, not for any *land*.'

'It's a cure against evil,' Mactalla said, with a reassuring tone.

'I don't know if I can help against evil,' she retorted. 'Some folks round here think I'm the evil one.'

'Folks are ignorant, Agnes. But ye and I know the truth.'

When Agnes saw Mactalla's honesty and his lack of prejudice, she let her guard down and grinned, and despite the deep crow's feet around her sunken squinty eyes, for a split second she looked like a girl again.

That afternoon, over wooden bowls of tea, Mactalla explained what he wanted to do.

SPEED

Whenever there was to be any gathering or business to attend to, it was Speed, the peregrin falcon, who conveyed the information. Sitting on a rock, with her silvery-soft wings tucked underneath, she and Mactalla discussed the latest mission.

And now, Speed propelled herself upwards on her assignment.

'See ye at the council!' she whistled, her cry carried away on the wind as she rose higher.

The following day, Tioram, Jette, Mactalla and the other Galaidean gathered. The spies gave the surprising report that Arioch's virtual cloak of invisibility appeared to be slipping – once or twice, they had caught a partial glimpse of him through the smoke that curled from a beach fire. It was a mystery.

Nevertheless, the next stage of the plan was about to launch. At the appointed time, Mactalla, Reef and Jette would navigate Mrs Kelly's old fishing boat out to sea, so as to create the illusion of 'smugglers' sailing towards land. They would head for the rocky beach on Arioch's bay, where they would stage a shipwreck and scatter 'contraband' on the beach. After that, they would swim to the next bay where *Coralee* would hide out and wait for the morning. The sky hunters and sea hounds would return to their lookout posts to wait for signs that Arioch had found the whisky. Then, when Mactalla received a signal, he and *Coralee* would set sail for Storm Island and rescue Oriole.

They just needed a storm.

PHANTOM

In the cave, dust motes hung motionless in the murky air and visibility was poor, so Oriole only gradually noticed when the gold of her feathers began to fade to a sickly orange-copper. And as her life drained away, the orange-copper faded to dirty-mustard-yellow and the stained-glass hues of her tail faded into watery pastels.

She was losing her powers, and that meant losing her usefulness as Arioch's 'rainbow bird'. Would her death be at the tip of a knife, or slow by starvation? There was one thing, however, she feared more than the way she would die: leaving this earth without an heir. She was the last of the winged prophets. As she looked down at the pitiful state of her failing body, the grief of her unborn chicks gnawed at her soul. Her physical body could be killed by the hand of Arioch, but she would actually die of a broken heart.

'Hold on!' she told herself. In that moment, no more than a nano-second, she saw a vision of an egg, her egg, and the tiniest spark of hope ignited in her heart.

'Fire bru!' Arioch demanded, in a voice twisted and gnarled by cruelty. 'Fire bru!'

She burbled and murmured. 'Please give me more time.'

He would give her extra time because fire bru must take a bit more magic. The next day, he repeated the order, grumbling with disgust that he had found less fish on the stick.

Oriole felt shockwaves shudder through her being – she was a smouldering wick and Arioch would soon extinguish her. No fire bru...less fish...Arioch's magic bird was losing its power.

In the dingy cave, Oriole struggled against the fog in her brain and invented excuses. She pleaded that waxberries would return her powers. (In fact, this was partially true; she was sick and the fruits would help her.)

'Lies!' hissed Arioch, spitting saliva and accusation in equal measure. By now, he realised his 'rainbow bird' would not last the winter. With this in mind, he gave her the ultimatum to 'magic up' meat and fire bru or face torture and death. Satisfied he had shaken the 'rainbow bird' out of her sloth, he fell asleep on his dirty bed.

He was fatter now, so he snored louder and Oriole slept less. Most nights her thoughts were pitiful, pathetic and distorted like a nightmare circus filled with macabre beings. She would often find herself pecking around in the arena of her mind for some crumb of truth, only to be descended on by black crows that devoured any small scraps of sanity. Sometimes, friends drifted in and out of the arena, but they were bizarrely deformed circus acrobats, their performances broken and wretched. If they were looking for her, they didn't show it, but even so, she was a phantom, unseen and unheard.

MOLLY GALLOWAY

One day, as Molly Galloway stood in her garden in the Bay of Goats, wondering whether to take in the washing, dark clouds thundered towards the land like army tanks. And then came the rain like miniature water bombs falling from the sky.

Wet and shivery with gooseflesh, Molly snatched armfuls of washing from the clothesline and hurtled her way to the back door where her children were waiting for her. They had been at the window, breathing on the glass and doodling pictures in the condensation, bored, pinched and hungry. It had been raining for months and the vegetables were maggotty, the potatoes were a black sludge and under an unforgiving, sunless sky, the fruit had stayed green and sour. Everything that touched the soil was putrified by the wet and the cold. Even the cattle had rotting feet. There were big gaps on the shelves of the local grocery store and what came in trucks from Glasgow was too expensive. Then came a bad flu and all the schools closed. Molly's daughter Fiona developed a nasty cough, which became a chest infection. When Fiona's temperature soared, Molly moved her sister out of their shared bedroom. She was about to go to the shop for more medicine when she saw two young men walking along the coastal road at the bottom of her garden.

'Hoi,' she shouted in greeting and they waved and stopped by her garden gate

Jock Campbell and Wilkie Burns were young men with red hair under their woolly hats who always wore kilts made from miles of tartan cloth that swung heavily in the rhythm of their gait. Great army boots and thick chunky socks covered their legs except for hairy, knobbly knees.

They were travelling from village to village to hold meetings and tell anyone (who was naive or stupid enough to listen) about the current de-gra-dation of soc-ie-ty and how the 'judgement of God' was 'now upon us' because of im-mor-ality. Sins like materialism and greed; too many televisions and cars, too much food and not enough campaigning against nuclear weapons, snollygosters or world hunger. If people were even half awake, they yawped, the social decay of the present day could be avoided. And it was no good to put hopes in the rainbow bird or even the seal people. If they ever existed in the first place, they would have left long ago because of im-mor-ality.

Folk christened them 'the prophets of doom'. And with their brash and arrogant teaching, everyone should have seen through them, but the possession of a cast-iron confidence, even when it is founded in self-deception, is a powerful and persuasive thing. A pea-soup gloom trailed in their wake. Folks shuffled from home to work, from work to the pub and from the pub to their bed. And the next day, it started all over again.

Molly regarded the two strangers at the bottom of her garden.

'Do ye know if there's anything happening in town tonight?' said Jock.

'I dinnae think so,' said Molly. 'Why do ye ask?'

Jock and Wilkie introduced themselves and told Molly of their 'mission'.

Molly tilted her head towards the young men and frowned. 'Are ye sure about this? she asked. 'How do ye know?'

Jock replied that no one had told them...it was unnecessary, since they could read 'the signs of the times'.

'If ye get smart,' he swaggered, 'ye'll see it for ye'sel'.'

His head's full of mince, Molly thought...doolally!

Jock rambled on about the departed rainbow bird and the present crisis in the Ardnamurchan.

Like a breadstick, Molly's patience snapped and she towered over them in anger, even though they were of a much greater height.

'Get away with ye!' she commanded, her face tingling with the rush of blood.

The startled laddies had just enough sense to obey and stomped down the road, their kilts in full swing.

How dare those bampots call us cursed! she thought. But deep inside, there was a nagging concern: what if folk believed them?

Molly went to the local shop, still on fire with indignation. Bay of Goats was a small village where everyone knew everyone else's business, so whoever she met asked about Fiona, and she followed her news with a warning about the two young lads. Just as she was about to leave, Mrs Kelly appeared in her saggy yellow cardigan and wellies.

'Hullo Mrs Kelly,' said Molly. 'How are ye?'

'Well, I got rid of my boat!'

'Good for ye!' said Molly, 'but excuse me, I must get back to Fiona.' She was about to go but thought better of it...she should warn the old lady about the dunderheids.

'Mrs Kelly,' said Molly. 'Watch out for two lads in kilts and big boots telling everyone we are all under a curse because of wickedness, and the "rainbow bird" and even the "seal people" have abandoned us,' and with that she raised an eyebrow to suggest the tragic absurdity of it all.

Already fit to burst with her latest news, Mrs Kelly could contain herself no longer. 'It was a "seal man" who took my boat,' she blurted excitedly, and everyone in the shop heard it. Generally, she had nothing important to say, so now her smile was as wide and wild as the Cheshire Cat's. The normal rhythm of the grocery store was temporarily suspended as everyone stopped what they were doing to stare at Mrs Kelly who stood on the shop's doormat in her yellow cardigan, looked more dishevelled than usual.

'Is this true, Mrs Kelly?' said Molly.

'Truer than true. And what's more, he was on a mission. Fergus Doone knows all about it.'

THE ENVOYS

Everyone agreed Cameron McDonald and Dr Murray should go – they were sensible folk who 'didnae get carried away'. Dr Murray particularly wanted to clear up the 'nonsense' about sickness being a curse.

Around the enormous kitchen table, Fergus Doone told them about Oriole, Arioch, Mactalla and the rescue plan...and furthermore, how the 'seal people' had not abandoned them.

Doctor Murray sat over a steaming cup of tea and a piece of carrot cake. His head was mostly bald except for a few wisps of hair that stuck out from the sides of his head. He peered through his small spectacles and over his bulging belly at the remains of his carrot cake and hoped there would be a second helping.

'Well, that is extraordinary news.' His piercing blue eyes examined everyone around the table. 'Has anyone made plans for what will happen to Oriole after she is rescued? She will need medical care and attention.'

'I'm in charge,' said Maggie, and turning to Dr Murray she added, 'but can you help?'

A team formed: *Coralee* was fitted out with medical supplies, Maggie's turret room was transformed into a little hospital, and most importantly, they prepared a rescue pack for Mactalla.

SHIPWRECK

'Fire bru!' bellowed Arioch. 'Get me fire bru!'

'It's on its way,' shivered Oriole. 'It just takes a little longer.'

'Yah!' he raged in disgust, savagely poking the fire and sending sparks in all directions.

'Three days. Get me fire bru in three days, or die!'

Oriole sat on her perch in silence. She was a wretched sight. Most of her colour had gone and she was losing feathers. Though weak and breathless, she fought to stay upright since falling would probably mean death.

The next day, Arioch went to the beach and found only one fish on the stick.

'Yah!' he seethed and made a fire. Later, as he finished his meal, dark ominous clouds began to descend on the island, so he made his way back to the cave.

Reef and Jette watched Arioch's beach from Seal Ridge. When the sea hounds saw the approaching storm, they torpedoed through the water to Mrs Kelly's old fishing boat, where Mactalla awaited their arrival. Soon the boat was doggedly chugging its way through the mounting choppy sea. Battling the waves was a bitter and tiring slog, but eventually they were in line with Arioch's Island; then they toiled even further towards the ocean, where they dropped the storm anchor. The boat was tub-shaped and storm resistant, but Mactalla and the sea hounds were tossed around like pebbles in the surf amid the deafening hullabaloo of howling wind, roaring sea and creaking vessel. In the fury of the tempest, Mactalla boomed that it was time.

They were driven blindly towards the island, but managed to glimpse a solid black mass of land silhouetted against the sky, and still further in, they caught sight of a familiar tree-line, the landmark they needed to guide them to Arioch's beach.

Jette steered towards the side of an outcrop of rocks, the boat pitched forward before the driving wind and then it happened: the vessel crashed on its portside and all three were thrown sideways. As soon as Mactalla regained balance, he lowered himself onto the rocks and swung Fergus's axe into the hull of the boat. After much cracking and creaking, the vessel began to flood with water. No one could speak or even hear themselves think in the pandemonium; they simply carried out what had been rehearsed in conversation many times before. Reef and Jette passed the wooden crate to Mactalla, who removed the bottles and scattered them on the beach away from the surf. Everything was done in order, but very slowly, as crashing wave upon crashing wave interrupted their every move.

Eventually, Mactalla and the sea hounds swam to *Coralee* and waited until morning. During the night, the squall, like a tiring monster, weakened and retreated, but even so, *Coralee* tossed and turned and no one slept.

THE GALLOWS

Arioch looked out from the mouth of his cave to survey the shore below. Large clumps of seaweed were washed up all over the beach along with bits of driftwood, broken tree branches and an orange bucket. A bucket would be handy, Arioch thought; he must go to examine it. He hoped it wasn't cracked.

He clawed his way down the rock face, pausing every few minutes to check whether the sea had washed up anything else more interesting than a bucket. Half-way down, he halted when he spotted the remains of a boat that was smashed up on the rocks; he watched it for some time, scanning for signs of life, and concluded that it was empty. The people on the vessel had surely drowned at sea. Near the boat, on the sandy shore, lay the splintered remains of a wooden crate and some amber coloured things that must have spilled out from the box. He trembled with feverish anticipation over what he might find and began to scramble down as fast as he could. When he reached the bottom, he hurriedly scratched his way through the shrubbery that hugged the foot of the cliff, and emerging bedraggled from the undergrowth, he ran towards the wreck. What a windfall! There were bottles of fire-bru scattered on the sand. His greed, like a partially submerged crocodile, fully surfaced, and drool dribbled in strings from between the crags of his teeth. '*Fie ya broooo...*' he droned raspily, savouring the sound of his own words.

The 'rainbow bird' sent for *fie ya brooo*.

One of the bottles swished around in the incoming tide, chinking, every few seconds, against a rock. Arioch gathered them up excitedly and counted: one, two, three, four, five. 'Five! Five!' he exclaimed. He noticed that one bottle had smashed; there was evidence of broken glass stuck in the sand and a cork that bobbed around in the shallows.

Other things had fallen out of the boat: an oar, a few buoys and a leather satchel. Arioch moved everything away from the shoreline and piled up his treasure a few metres away under some bushes, then he swung the satchel, with its long leather strap, across his body. He filled it with two bottles of fire-bru and carefully ascended the cliff face.

Oriole heard Arioch groping his way towards the entrance of the cave and then watched, incredulously, as he emptied his satchel. She could only marvel at the miraculous timing; the whisky had saved her. For the time being, Arioch would keep her alive.

Arioch wrenched the cork from the bottle with his teeth and spat it on the ground; then he thirstily tipped back his head and gulped huge slugs of fire-bru. He prepared himself to collect the remaining bottles from the beach, and so slung the satchel across his body and criss-crossed it with a coil of rope.

Before he left the cave, Arioch looked at Oriole and, for the first and last time, their eyes met. For a brief moment, it was a window into the unending frozen wasteland of his cruel and desolate soul. Then, he turned towards the entrance of the cave and staggered sideways. His descent was wobbly – there was something wrong. He tried to think, but something was stupefying his mind. Should he return to the cave or carry on? His brain was frozen by indecision. He stumbled, grazed himself on a rock, and groped around for a handhold, but the rope he wore across his body had become tangled on a solitary branch, so it prevented him from reaching anything.

As he tried to free the rope, he lost his footing and

slid a second time. When this happened, a metal buckle on the satchel jammed in the crack of a rock and the coils of the rope tightened around his neck and burnt his skin. Now the leather strap pulled him from one direction whilst the coils of the rope pulled him from another. He was choking. His toes felt around for a foothold and he was relieved to find a thin branch that grew out of a crack in the rock. But, as he perched, it slowly loosened under the pressure of his weight and small lumps of stony soil trickled to the beach below.

Then something even more terrifying happened: it felt as though his arms were rapidly turning to lead and the blood in his veins to hot treacle. He was almost paralysed; his body oozed cold, sour sweat. The branch under his foot suddenly gave way – not that he felt it, he only heard it, for now his legs were completely numb.

All of this happened in only a few minutes, but for Arioch time took on an infinite quality. The boundaries of his inner and outer world blurred: inwardly, he felt a hideous magnetic force dragging him down into what seemed like a pitch-black mineshaft. In the outer world he was suspended like a fly trapped in a cobweb of rope, branches and leather strap. He heard an unearthly horrible sound, like someone being strangled; was it coming from him? His lungs were on fire; he wanted to scream with the searing pain, but all he could manage was a tortured rasp – he was suffocating...and in the black hole he was plummeting down, down, and down – the falling was unbearable – death presented itself as both an escape from falling, but the beginning of an endless nightmare – and then...THUD. He hit the bottom.

Arioch was a black hole of greed who tried to fill the huge chasm inside himself with what he had stolen, but he remained a vast empty-nothing-place, until finally, the black hole that had been Arioch imploded and he ceased to be.

THE RESCUE

J ette scanned the island from the lookout at Seal Ridge. Then, in her sea-hound form, she streamed through the water until she surfaced about twenty-five metres from the shore, with only her eyes and a few whiskers showing. Arioch had salvaged things from the wreckage including the bottles. Good, she thought, but what now? There were no signs of life on the island, so she returned to the lookout to examine the beach and the cliff from a different angle. The watchpost was in line with the western tip of the island and from there she could see the abandoned boat and above it, the cliff face that led to Arioch's cave. Scanning the whole area, she caught sight of a reddish thing that dangled high up on the rock face; it seemed to be trapped in a jumbled mess of branches and other unrecognisable stuff. She stared hard at the tangle, trying to make sense of it, and all at once the shape of a red limb came into focus. It was hanging just above a thicker trunk-like thing of the same colour. Then she understood: it was an arm and a leg. It was Arioch. He was only partly visible in the mass of twigs and shrubbery, but the sight of his lifeless body parts made her sure of one thing: he was dead. This sudden and unexpected revelation triggered a rush of relief and adrenaline. Submerged, she shot through the water like a ballistic missile on course for *Coralee* and the others.

Mactalla and Reef were leaning over the edge of the boat, waiting in suspense.

'Arioch's...dead,' she said, catching her breath.

Silently, Reef set sail whilst Jette climbed aboard. They dropped anchor in the bay of Storm Island and Mactalla waded ashore with Maggie and Dr Murray's rescue pack. The ascent to Arioch's cave was slow and arduous, but he made steady progress and finally he reached the corpse.

Mactalla marvelled at the literal outcome of what he had once predicted. Arioch had hung himself on his own gallows. The sight of the corpse triggered memories of all those soul-searching nights on Corran's Mount where the council had wrestled with the same questions: what should they do about Arioch? When was the right time to stop evil? Were they, unlike their ancestors, the un-brave ones? Was it their fault that Arioch had kidnapped Oriole?

Evil prevails when good folk do nothing. And now Mactalla regarded Arioch, who was looking down, through his dead eyes, to his final doom. They had found a way.

He eventually arrived at the cave entrance. Silkies have bigger eyes than land folk, thus it takes longer for their vision to adjust from light to dark. For a while, he stared blindly into a foul smelling black hole.

The shadowy figure of Mactalla appeared before Oriole. When Oriole was first captured she believed that the Galaidean would rescue her but as the quicksand of death pulled her down, she slowly gave in to its fate. And now the phantom of her friend had somehow broken through into her world. She warily searched her heart for the smallest crumb of hope, anything to convince herself that this vision was not another tormenting illusion.

Mactalla, whose eyes were beginning to adjust to the dimness, heard a slight rustle of feathers and then recognised the faint outline of Oriole sitting on a perch.

'Oriole!' he softly cried. Mactalla's warm, salty voice broke into her miasma of despair and she jolted. Unable to reply, she feebly whimpered and then fainted.

Mactalla rushed forward and set about cutting her

free from the chain. Now that his eyesight had grown accustomed to the gloom, he saw Oriole's wretched condition and the urgency of the situation. He swiftly anchored his rope on a boulder, harnessed Oriole to his body and abseiled down the cliff face; on the way, she drifted in and out of consciousness and missed the sight of Arioch's corpse as it hung from the shrubbery. He descended slowly at first, but then more rapidly as he reached the lower, gentler slopes.

At the foot of the mountain, Jette met Mactalla. While waiting for him, she had explored the beach and discovered Arioch's coracle hidden in a cave. They floated the tiny vessel on the water and lowered Oriole into it; from there Reef and Jette coasted the boat to *Coralee*, where Mactalla, who had swam from the shore, received them.

The sea hounds were shaken at the sight of Oriole. She was barely alive. They wrapped her in blankets and, once under sail, fed her with droplets of honey-water. This went on for hours. She awakened for only a few moments at a time. Her speech was delirious: 'fire-bru...no fire-bru...Tioram.'

By the time *Coralee* reached their destination and moored, it was dark. Mactalla carried Oriole to the turret at the top of the house. He stayed over the next several weeks, working with Fergus here and there, but staying close to Oriole and her nurse Maggie. Tioram,

Clamhan and the other sky hunters often came with supplies of waxberries. Agnes Fife called in and treated Oriole with natural medicines. Mactalla spent long afternoons reciting tales from *The Legend*: 'Shona of the sea', 'Camhana of the hills' and 'Cath the great sky hunter', to name but a few. Reef and Jette visited often – friendship, too, was healing the trauma of her ordeal.

It was a wonderful day when, months later, Oriole fluttered, albeit unsteadily, to the balcony to soak in the soft autumn sun. Every step forward was a celebration: one day, she began to turn the palest gold and on another occasion, she sang for the first time, a warbled fragile tune. And winter came...but new life was already sprouting in the soil of Oriole's heart.

Mactalla thought about how Oriole's kidnapping had brought the land folk and the Galaidean together: Arioch's crime had united two worlds like never before.

'Unity brings justice to victory,' he murmured to himself and smiled.

A few days after Oriole's rescue, Fergus and Mactalla sailed to Storm Island to cut Arioch's body free. They hauled it up to his foul cave and left it there.

Before departing, Mactalla spilled the drugged whisky into the ground and watched the poison drain away.

ORIOLE'S SONG

By springtime, Oriole's colours had almost fully returned and she could sing again. The Ardnamurchan was in a great thaw and in the warm part of those days, she sat with Mactalla on the turret balcony discussing the future and the need for hope to be restored to the Ardnamurchan.

'It would seem to the world,' Oriole said, 'as though Arioch wanted me for no other reason than to satisfy his own selfish greed. But I spent long enough imprisoned to realise darker forces were at work. I *saw* the mind behind his mind. He was a black hole with a bigger appetite than himself; he couldn't bear for *any* goodness to exist, he had to swallow it. He stole me to steal hope itself. Folk cannae face life or fight death without it. Mactalla, I must go with *Coralee* to the

Highlands and Islands. I must fly again and restore hope.'

ON A STRETCH of lawn that overlooked the bay, folk had erected an arch of flowering branches that framed a pedestal for Oriole. Mactalla took his place next to her and Clamhan perched on the other side. Reef and Jette in their sea-hound form waited in *Coralee* and watched from a distance (sea hounds are much shyer than silkies and not accustomed to mixing with land folk).

The local laird, Hamish Mcfadden, opened the farewell event with a speech about how, 'together we have learnt that where there is unity, there is strength. With a common purpose we have fought shoulder to shoulder and we have won back our hope and our future.'

'Yaldi! Yaldi!' the folk cried, and the laird, who was not usually cheered for his public speaking, felt quite heroic (his last speech had been made at the opening ceremony of the *Ardnamurchan Farm and Country Show*, which he launched every year, but this was much more exciting). He officially thanked the Doones, Mrs Kelly, Agnes Fife, Dr Murray and Cameron McDonald for their contribution towards the rescue of the 'rainbow bird'. After that, the rumours about Agnes Fife being a witch were dispelled and Mrs Kelly had humans for friends instead of just geese, so she bought a pair of shoes and a new cardigan.

After the laird had made his speech, he caught sight of two young men hanging around the fringes of the gathering. Jock Campbell and Wilkie Burns. He puffed his chest and raised a disapproving eyebrow in their direction. The land folk followed the laird's stern gaze to the two young men, who by this time wished the ground would give way and swallow them up. However, no one had time to think about Jock and Wilkie, for suddenly Oriole's breast expanded, her head tilted upwards, and as she opened her beak, a song poured forth, a splendid and glorious song that filled the bay with something like golden mist.

On the last note, Oriole rose upwards and circled the bay like a swirling rainbow, before settling on *Coralee*. This was Oriole's gift to the town, a new song for a new day.

When it finally ended, some wept because they could not bear for such a beautiful song to stop and wished they could spend the rest of their days just listening to Oriole sing. Others said that Oriole's song chased away sadness and if the odd gloomy day were ever to creep in, the remembrance would be enough to return them to feelings of wellbeing. Some hardly spoke for days and went about their work in a dreamlike state.

Much to the delight of the crowd, the laird invited Mactalla to speak.

'Ardnamurchan folk,' said Mactalla, smiling radiantly, 'ye are truly Galaidean. Never stop believing, for as an ancient silkie once said, "there is a place where sea meets land and truth meets legend".' Every eye was fixed on him and every heart stored his words like treasure.

As *Coralee* was setting sail and the people were waving their goodbyes, Fergus Doone felt a tug on his sleeve. It was Mrs Kelly, who looked up at him with a twinkly-eyed grin.

'Mr Doone, my Robbie left a leather satchel on the boat. Did ye find it?'

MACTALLA'S FAREWELL

The Company of Writers met to discuss Oriole's story and agreed that it was destined for the pages of the sacred book. Mactalla spent long afternoons with them as they recorded every detail, and when Oriole returned, she was to give a full account along with Jette and Reef.

As Mactalla set his sight on the sea's horizon, his eyes glazed over. He thought of the song,

I am a man on the land,
I am a silkie in the sea.

He sighed deeply. A weary sigh. His heart yearned for freedom from these earthly ties. He remembered the death of his father, Tunnag, and the years of watching the seas for seal hunters. And deep within, he sensed the call of Great North. Mactalla walked from Seal House to the water wearing the unmistakable appearance of one who was about to return home; others recognised the signs and followed him. Skully, his son, walked by his side.

'Lead them well, Skully. The favour of Corran the Galad is on ye. The favour of Mactalla is on ye,' and he removed his long sealskin coat and gave it to his son. 'Wear it well, Skully.'

Kelde, one of the Company of Writers, stood next to Skully. Unexpectedly, Mactalla instinctively knew the final destiny of his own skin – although he had not known it a few moments before.

'Kelde, I bequeath my skin to *The Legend*. I want to tell the story of Oriole, forever.' Kelde nodded and both understood. Others from the village gathered around and there were affectionate farewells on both sides, but Mactalla couldn't linger.

Standing on the edge of the shore, Mactalla looked down at his feet, feet that were touching the land for the very last time, and he faced the sea. The crossing bridge appeared before his eyes. Before walking into the water, he began to sing the sacred hymn that all silkies sing on their return to Great North.

The Journey Home

'From the sea came I,
To the sea I return,
The land borrowed me,
And, I borrowed thee,
No more a man on land
I am a silkie in the sea.'

Mactalla's voice was low and melancholic and his song filled the bay, heartbreaking and unbearably beautiful. He walked slowly into the sea and by the time the water covered his chest, the waves parted and took him into their arms.

There is a holy place known only to silkies, where they go to give up their skins. At the appointed time, Kelde took Mactalla's skin and pages were prepared for *The Legend*. Everyone awaited Oriole's return.

SAORSA – LIBERTY

I t was late summer. Mactalla had gone home to Great North several months before and Skully had succeeded him as leader of the silkies. One fine afternoon, he sensed the need to go to Mactalla's old watchtower, so he walked through the forest along the pine-needle path towards the lighthouse.

He stood on the black rock under the raw blue sky with seaspray billowing all around him. And just like Mactalla, he watched the sea. A little speck appeared on the horizon. When it glinted in the sun, he realised it was the golden bird on *Coralee*'s sail. Before long, he saw Jette waving and beckoning him. Wading into the water, he boarded *Coralee*, but he was unprepared for the sight that awaited him. Oriole was there and her appearance was more resplendent and dazzling than ever.

'Greetings, Skully,' said Oriole. Her voice was rich, vibrant, and strong like a stream of rushing water, only it wasn't water, but life itself.

'Greetings, Oriole...we longed for this day,' said Skully. 'Ye are most welcome on this island. It is your home.' He paused, sensing that Oriole held a secret that would surely explain her brilliance.

'Oriole,' he said with a questioning air, 'ye shine like the noonday sun; ye look quite marvellous to me.'

Oriole lowered her head towards her folded wing and opened it outwards. 'This is Saorsa,' said Oriole. And now Skully understood the reason for her radiance. Skully kneeled before mother and child.

'Liberty,' he said (for that is what Saorsa means in the Highland language). Saorsa tilted her small face towards Skully and cheeped.

'Liberty and freedom for all,' said Oriole. 'Your father is great among the silkies, for he fought with the strength of the Galaidean to restore hope to the Ardnamurchan. He was the true voice of his father, Great North. He is renamed Mactalla the Great, and he has honoured us with his skin to tell the story.'

Over the months that followed Oriole and Saorsa, Jette and Reef, Tioram and Clamhan along with *Coralee*, stayed on Seal Island as guests of the silkies. Oriole spent many days with the Company of Writers telling them her story, including the journey with Reef and Jette across the Islands and Highlands.

On her voyage, Oriole had witnessed the blanket of despair that had covered the land, and how, in the absence of hope, the folk had begun to die on the inside to the point where they were neither living or dead, neither black or white, but grey, all grey. In every village, she sang over the land folk, painting rainbows in the skies above their houses, shops and village centres, and her songs chased away the shadow. Her coming was a tsunami of life and colour, and, once again, laughter was heard in the land.

Oriole told the Company of Writers about Orion, her mate and Saorsa's father. Soon, he would join her in the land of the Ardnamurchan.

Kelde wrote the story of Oriole and added it to *The Legend* and on one late summer's evening, there was a gathering in Seal House to hear Skully read it. The telling of 'Oriole's Song' was a grand, historical event: the first time a new story had been added to *The Legend* in the lifetimes of those present. It was a story of evil laid bare and a land devoid of hope; they wept for their beloved friend, Mactalla, but the story brought them closer to him.

And, by the end of the reading all praised Kelde, who had crafted the story, and they stood in honour of

Mactalla because his life lived on. There were cheers for the Galaidean and the land folk who had fought together against such a force of evil.

Oriole flew to a high perch that had been especially set in place, and all heads turned towards her. A warm breeze rippled across Seal House as she flapped her resplendent wings. Her golden head and body shimmered and her full train of feathers, in jewelled rainbow colours, swished and rustled as she settled on the perch.

'Skully, Jette, and Tioram,' she said. 'Ye are the Galaidean of Ardnamurchan and ye are worthy of your name. I was the smouldering wick whose flame was almost snuffed out, but hope was restored and hope has given birth to freedom.' Her noble head turned towards Saorsa as she spoke. Then she ascended in flight to circle above the gathering, all the while singing:

> 'Live the story and let the story live on.
> Remember, there is a place where sea
> meets land and truth meets legend.'

She sang these words many times over, and each time she repeated them, those who heard felt stronger and wiser and freer and happier. And everyone knew, though they didn't know how, that for the Ardnamurchan, this was a new beginning.

NOTES

JETTE AND REEF

1. There are a few rare accounts of humans who witnessed the appearance of the bridge and the phenomenon of the crossing. No one knows why certain people have seen it – whether they have an unusual gift, or whether it is written in their destiny, or whether the veil that separates this world from the realm of the sea creatures becomes unexplainably thin, or maybe there is another explanation. Nevertheless, due to the sacred nature of the event, those who encountered the wonder generally didn't talk about it.

SEA-HOUND COVE

1. In 1828, 26 families who lived as smallhold tenants in the Ben Hiant area of the Ardnamurchan were evicted from their homes by the landowner who wanted to use the area for more profitable sheep farming. The evictions were particularly cruel. One woman with special needs was bricked into her house to be starved when she refused to leave. Some of the refugees were given small patches of wasteland to farm, whilst others were forced to emigrate to the colonies.

In the late 1840s, tenants in the Swordle Bay area of Ardnamurchan were made to build new houses to live in. The building requirements were high quality and expensive but by 1851 the tenants had fulfilled their obligation and owed no arrears of rent.

But, two years later they were forced to leave and many ended up homeless in the barren coastland of Sanna.

This sad chapter of Scottish history has become known as the

Highland Clearances. Sir James Milles Riddell was the proprietor responsible for clearing the Swordles as well as the Ben Hiant townships.

The people who fled the Ardnamurchan under such circumstances were not of a rough uneducated type. *The Inverness Courier*, a Scottish newspaper, reported the voyage of the ship *Brilliant* carrying emigrants to Australia. 105 of the passengers, from the Ardnamurchan, were said to be of excellent moral character with significant knowledge of agriculture, sheep, and cattle management, and were deemed the most valuable people to ever leave the shores of Great Britain.

History of the Highland Clearances. Written by Alexander Mackenzie. Pages 232–234, and 286. Courtesy of Internet Archive. University of California Libraries.

CLOUD AND THE KING

1. Dunadd is an atmospheric hill fort of the Dark Age Kingdom of Dál Riata. Situated in modern-day Argyll, it stretches north to the Ardnamurchan, west to N.Ireland, and south to the Mull of Kintyre. A footprint in the rock marks the place where the Gaelic kings were symbolically married to the land they were to rule.

PRISONER

1. There is an allegedly true story written about Scotland's first Christian missionary, St Columba, who gave a man a stick, which he had sharpened and blessed. He told the man that when it was placed in either woodland or river, it would not kill cattle or man but wild beasts and fish. The stick miraculously speared the said animals and provided for the man and his family, alleviating them of their poverty. Sadly, though, he lost the stick and became poor once again!

The Life Of Saint Columba, Founder of Hy. Written by Adamnan. Edited by William Reeves. Published 1874. Book II,

NOTES

Chapter XXXVIII (38) page 63. Uploaded to the Internet Archive by the University of Toronto Scanning Center.

ACKNOWLEDGMENTS

Andrew Gill, I don't have enough space to detail your support and faith in me. But thank you endlessly.

Claire Wingfield, Editor. What would I do without you?

Tracey Groves. Friend and Illustrator. Thank you for falling in love with the story and especially Oriole.

Paul Manning of Amews Falconry, Hampshire, for inspirational talks on eagles.

For the people of Ardnamurchan: you don't know it, but you inspire me.

ABOUT THE AUTHOR

Kay Gill is a Hampshire girl although globetrotting is one of her passions.

She lived in the Ardnamurchan for a while and was inspired to write The Legend.

Married to Andrew, she is the proud mother of four children (seven including spouses) and seven grandchildren. Her dogs Bonnie, and Tyson who is now resting in peace, were great sea hounds!

A few words and thoughts about some of the threads that you will see running through anything that the author writes...

She loves to pen a story in the genre of magical realism, although for her, she just writes it as she sees it. And on the page, words become portals into new dimensions.

Words themselves, and language, are the fabric of culture. Not just official 'mainstream' words, but those that are colloquial, ethnic, endangered, or worthy antiques.

Words are also a moveable feast; Shakespeare knew

that, and he enriched the English language with thousands of his own additions.

Most importantly, words possess the ability to summon the bestest version of self. For words call forth true identity and banish false, and it follows that true identity sprouts wings to fly in true destiny.

Additionally, Kay possesses a fascination for the folklore of different nations. In the past, the mythology of Scotland was largely communicated through oral tradition, and so this book is a literary celebration and tribute to one of the national treasures of Scottish heritage.

Please help to spread the word and consider leaving a review of this book online. These are a huge help to authors. You can reach Kay on tresorpress@gmail.com to share your thoughts on the story.

instagram.com/kaygillauthor

Ingram Content Group UK Ltd.
Milton Keynes UK
UKHW011845100723
424870UK00001B/1

9 781739 375300